Scholastic

LITERACY PLACE

SNAPSHOTS

SUPER SOLVERS

Lights! Camera! Action!

SNAPSHOTS

Come to
a Sports Arena

Our actions tell
about us.

Close-ups

We find out what we like to do.

Talent Show

We find out what we can do well.

Make Your Mark

When we try our best, we find out
how much we can do.

Trade Books

The following books accompany this *Snapshots* SourceBook.

Fantasy
Chester's Way
by Kevin Henkes

Fantasy
**Frog and Toad
Are Friends** Caldecott Honor
by Arnold Lobel

Realistic Fiction
A Birthday Basket for Tía
by Pat Mora
illustrated by Cecily Lang

Big Book

Realistic Fiction
Max Found Two Sticks
by Brian Pinkney

Close-ups

We find out what we like to do.

Find out what other kids like to do.

Read about a boy who loves baseball. Then meet two real-life baseball players.

TOP TEN

by Karen Edwards

How do second graders spend their free time? Children in Texas, California, New York, and Tennessee were asked that question. Their answers show that they don't spend all their time watching TV! What they like best is to play!

PLAYING BALL
Christian Velasquez
New York City

PLAYING BALL
Andrea West
Plano, Texas

SKATING
Christina Vargas
and Anthony Harris
New York City

RIDING BIKES
Jessica West
Corryton, Tennessee

PLAYING BALL
Russell McDaniel
Azusa, California

Let's Go Outside!

What do second graders play when they are outside? Both boys and girls like playing team sports like basketball and soccer. Russell McDaniel from Azusa, California, loves being the catcher on his baseball team.

Others like activities that they can do alone or with just a few friends. Christina Vargas and Anthony Harris from New York City love in-line skating. Anthony says, "I do tricks and turns and I go fast!" Many children love bike riding.

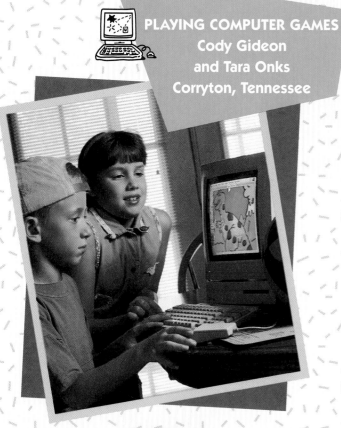

PLAYING COMPUTER GAMES
Cody Gideon
and Tara Onks
Corryton, Tennessee

READING
Jeanne Pan
Plano, Texas

Playing Inside

For indoor fun, most second graders play with their toys and games. Cody Gideon and Tara Onks from Corryton, Tennessee, take turns with computer games.

A lot of children, like Jeanne Pan from Plano, Texas, love to read their favorite stories.

PLAYING WITH TOYS
Richard Cantley
Corryton, Tennessee

Crafts and drawing also rate high. Ronald Draper of New York City says, "Drawing is a lot of fun. I can draw cats, dogs, and other things."

DRAWING AND CRAFTS
Ronald Draper
New York City

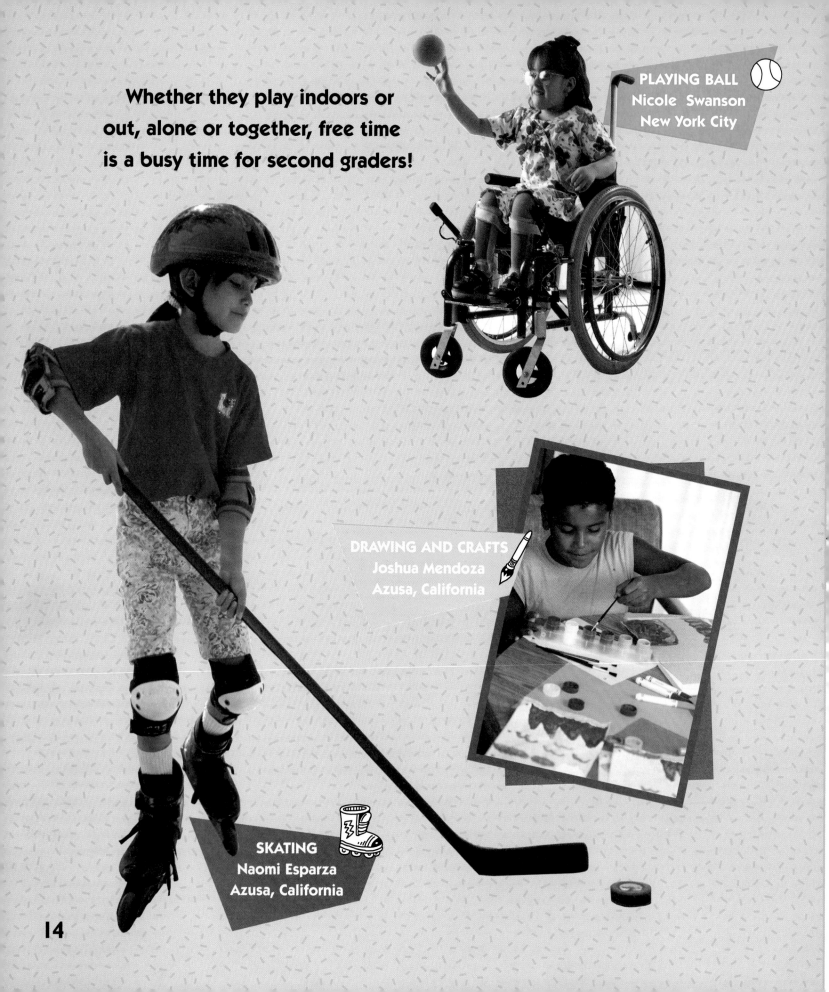

Whether they play indoors or out, alone or together, free time is a busy time for second graders!

PLAYING BALL
Nicole Swanson
New York City

DRAWING AND CRAFTS
Joshua Mendoza
Azusa, California

SKATING
Naomi Esparza
Azusa, California

14

The Vote Is In!

Here is a graph that shows the top ten
activities for all the second graders questioned.
Is your favorite activity on the graph?

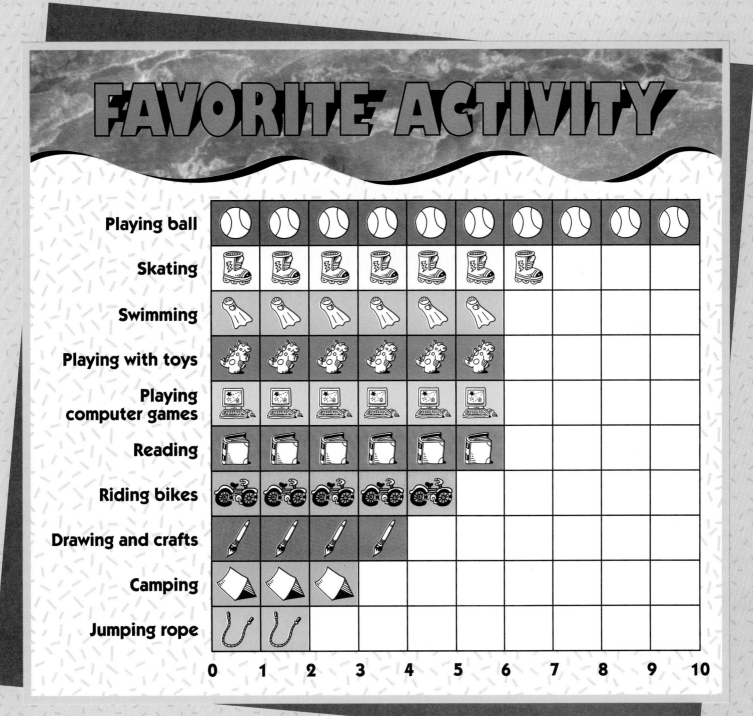

FAVORITE ACTIVITY

	0	1	2	3	4	5	6	7	8	9	10
Playing ball											
Skating											
Swimming											
Playing with toys											
Playing computer games											
Reading											
Riding bikes											
Drawing and crafts											
Camping											
Jumping rope											

A, MY NAME

A, my name is Alice,
And my friend's name is Al.
We come from Anaheim,
And we like acting.

B, my name is Belinda,
And my friend's name is Bart.
We come from Boston,
And we like biking.

C, my name is Carmella,
And my friend's name is Carlos.
We come from Chicago,
And we like canoeing.

D, my name is Dixie,
And my friend's name is Dave.
We come from Denver,
And we like dancing.

E, my name is Emma,
And my friend's name is Earl.
We come from El Paso,
and we like eating.

16

IS ALICE

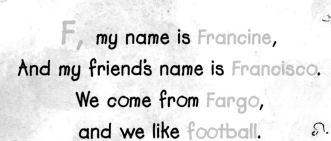

F, my name is Francine,
And my friend's name is Francisco.
We come from Fargo,
and we like football.

G, my name is Gwendolyn,
And my friend's name is Gus.
We come from Greensboro,
and we like gardening.

H, my name is Hee Sun,
And my friend's name is Henry.
We come from Hoboken,
And we like hiking.

I, my name is India,
And my friend's name is Ike.
We come from Indianapolis,
and we like ice skating.

J, my name is Julia,
And my friend's name is Jim.
We come from Jacksonville,
And we like jumping.

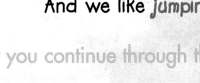

Now you continue through the alphabet.

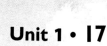

Ronald Morgan Goes to Bat

by Patricia Reilly Giff

illustrated by Susanna Natti

AWARD
WINNING

Book

Baseball started today.

Mr. Spano said everyone could play.

"Even me?" I asked.

And Tom said,

"You're letting Ronald Morgan play?

He can't hit, he can't catch.

He can't do anything."

Mr. Spano looked at me.

"Everyone," he said.

"Yahoo!" I yelled.

I pulled on my red and white shirt,
the one that says GO TEAM GO,
and ran outside to the field.
"Two things," Mr. Spano told us.
"Try hard, and keep your eye on the ball."

Then it was time to practice.

Michael was up first.

He smacked the ball with the bat.

The ball flew across the field.

"Good," said Mr. Spano.

"Great, Slugger!" I yelled.

"We'll win every game."

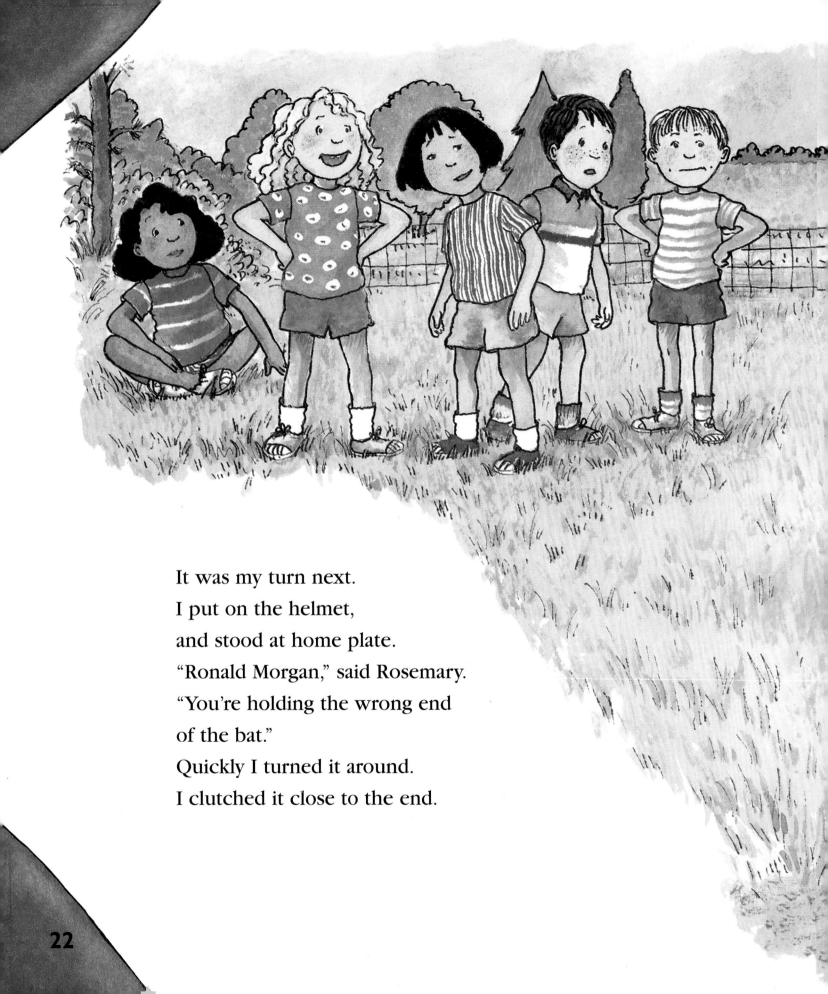

It was my turn next.
I put on the helmet,
and stood at home plate.
"Ronald Morgan," said Rosemary.
"You're holding the wrong end
of the bat."
Quickly I turned it around.
I clutched it close to the end.

22

Whoosh went the first ball.

Whoosh went the second one.

Wham went the third.

It hit me in the knee.

"Are you all right?" asked Michael.

But I heard Tom say,

"I knew it.

Ronald Morgan's the worst."

At snack time,

we told Miss Tyler about the team.

"I don't hit very well," I said.

And Rosemary said,

"The ball hits him instead."

Everybody laughed, even me.

I shook my head.

"I hope it doesn't happen again."

Miss Tyler gave me some raisins.

"You have to hit the ball

before it hits you," she said.

We played every day.

I tried hard, but the ball came fast.

I closed my eyes and swung.

"If only he could hit the ball once,"
Rosemary said.

And Billy shook his head.

I couldn't tell them I was afraid
of the ball.

"Go team go," I whispered.

One day, the team sat on the grass.
We watched the third grade play.
They were big, they were strong,
they were good.
Johnny hit a home run,
and Joy tagged a man out.

"We'll never hit like that," said Tom.

And Rosemary said,

"We'll never catch like that either."

But I said,

"Our team is the best."

Mr. Spano nodded.

"That's the spirit, Ronald."

Mr. Spano told us,
"Now we'll run the bases.
Rosemary, you can go first."
Rosemary went fast.
She raced for first base.
"Terrific, Speedy!" I yelled.

"Let me go next," I said.

"I can do that, too."

But the field was muddy.

My sneaker came off.

Jimmy said, "That kid's running
bases the wrong way."

And Tom yelled, "Ronald Morgan.
You're heading for third base."

The next day, we worked on catching.

I was out in left field.

While I waited, I found a stick,

and started to scratch out the mud.

I wrote G for go.

I wrote G for great.

Our team is the best, I thought.

Then I wrote H for hit.

H for home run.

If only I could do that.

Just then I heard yelling.

Someone had hit the ball.

"Catch it, Ronald!" Tom shouted.

I put down the stick.

I put up my mitt.

Too late.

The ball sailed into the trees.

Mr. Spano took us for ice cream.

"You deserve it for trying," he said.

"Our team is really good."

I had a chocolate cone.

Michael's a slugger, I thought.

And Rosemary can really run.

But I'm still afraid of the ball.

On the way home,

we saw some kids playing ball.

"Want to hit a few?" Michael asked.

I shook my head.

"Maybe I won't play ball anymore."

Michael said, "We need you.

You have spirit.

You help the team feel good."

"But how can we win?" I asked.

"I can't even hit the ball."

I saw my father and ran to catch up.

"See you, Michael," I said.

My father asked, "How's the champ?"

"I'm the worst," I said.

"I was the worst, too," said my father.

"But then..."

"What?"

My father laughed. "I stopped closing my eyes when I swung."

"Maybe that's what I do."

"How about a little practice?" he asked.

We went into the yard.

My father threw me some balls.

I missed the first one...

I missed the second.

And then...

I opened my eyes and swung.
Crack went the ball.
"Ouch!" went my father.
"You hit me in the knee."
"Home run!" yelled my mother.

"Sorry," I said.

"Hey, I did it!"

My father rubbed his knee.

"You certainly did," he said.

I ran to pick up the ball.

"See you later," I said.

My father smiled.

"Where are you going?"

I grabbed the bat.

"Some kids are playing ball.

I think I'll hit a few."

I looked back.

"And you know what else?

I guess I'll stay on the team.

I have spirit...

and sometimes I can hit the ball.

Mike was right.

I think they need me."

Babe Ruth

Baseball
Greats

BASEBALL
IMMORTALS

1936

OUTFIELDER
BABE RUTH

Team:
New York Yankees

Born:
February 6, 1895

NEW YORK YANKEES OUTFIELDER
Born: 2/6/95 Died: 8/16/48
Height: 6'2" Weight: 215 Bats: L. Throws: L.

BABE RUTH

NO. 1

Considered by many to be the greatest player of all-time, Ruth revolutionized baseball by making the home run a major offensive weapon. Before Ruth's arrival, teams relied mostly on speed to score runs. In a 22-year career (1914-35), spent mostly with the Yankees, Ruth hit 714 home runs and a lifetime slugging average of .690. A .342 lifetime hitter, he ranks second on the all-time list in home runs and runs batted in and first in walks and slugging percentage. Ruth led the American League in home runs 12 times and his 60 homers in 1927 is the record for a 154-game season. Ruth also was a standout pitcher with the Red Sox before being shifted to the outfield.

Which Hall of Famer was known as "Double X?"

Answer: Jimmy Foxx

Height: 6 feet, 2 inches
Weight: 215 pounds

Bats: Left
Throws: Left

Juan Gonzalez

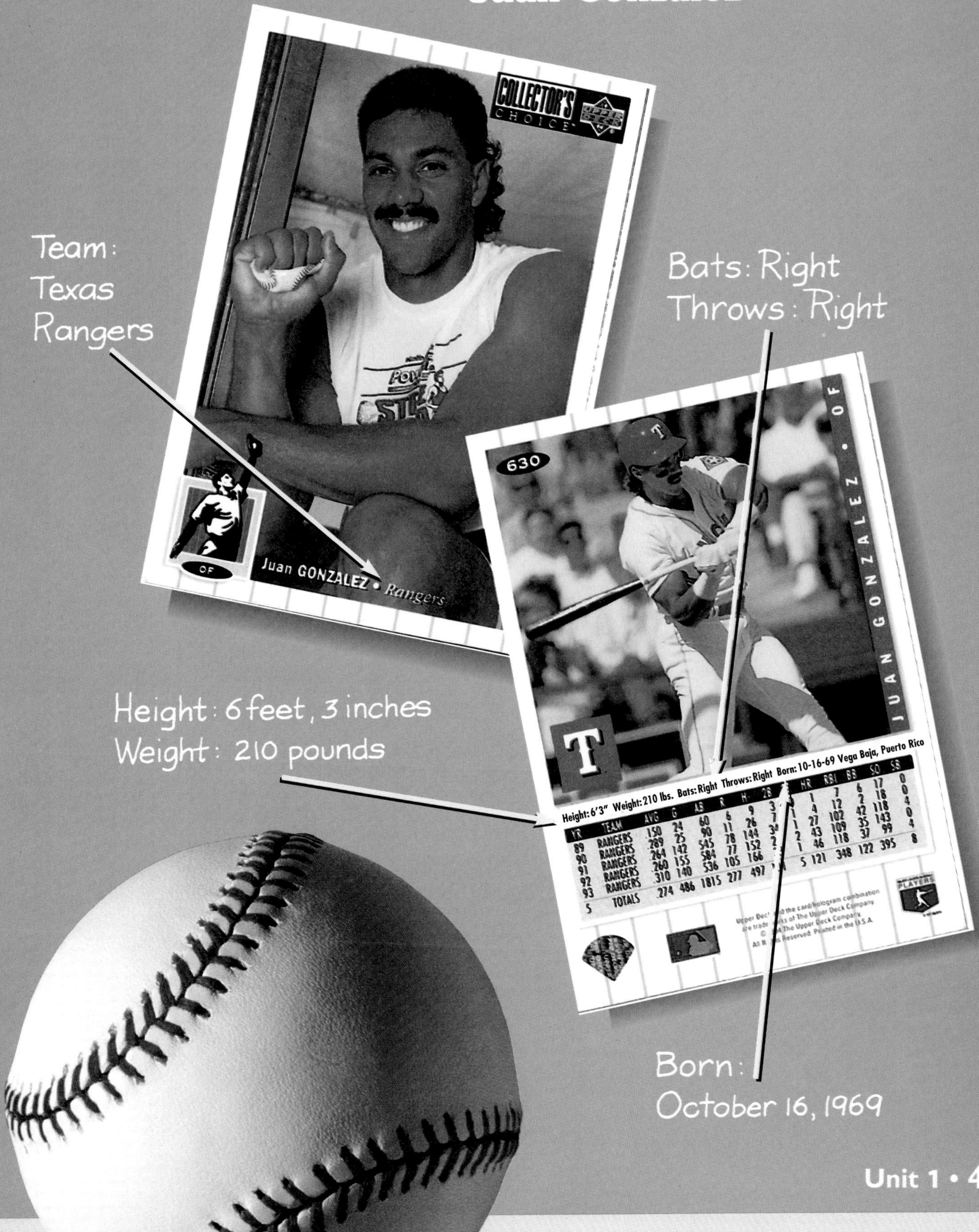

Team:
Texas
Rangers
Bats: Right
Throws: Right
Height: 6 feet, 3 inches
Weight: 210 pounds
Born:
October 16, 1969
COLLECTOR'S CHOICE
OF
Juan GONZALEZ • Rangers
630
JUAN GONZALEZ • OF
Height: 6'3" Weight: 210 lbs. Bats: Right Throws: Right Born: 10-16-69 Vega Baja, Puerto Rico

Talent Show

We find out what we can do well.

See how Ruby learns that she is special. Then read about another girl who can do anything!

Laugh with two friends as they try to make the team.

Click! Meet Bruce Thorson, a photographer.

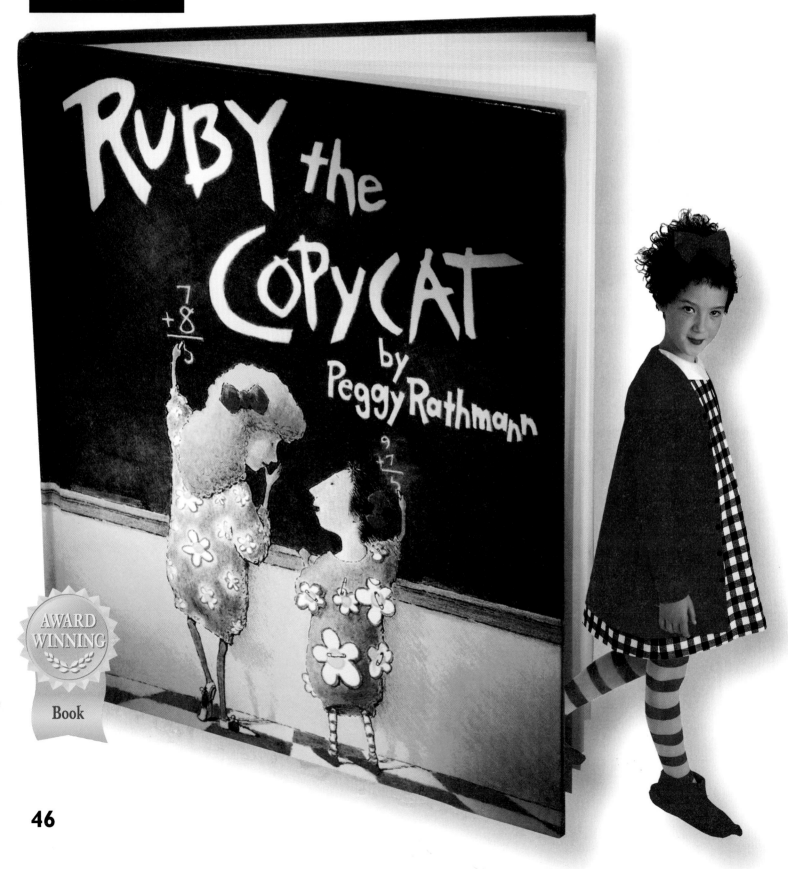

AWARD
WINNING

Book

Monday was Ruby's first day in Miss Hart's class.

"Class, this is Ruby," announced Miss Hart.

"Ruby, you may use the empty desk behind Angela.
Angela is the girl with the pretty red bow in her hair."

Angela smiled at Ruby.

Ruby smiled at Angela's bow and tiptoed to her seat.

"I hope everyone had a pleasant weekend," said
Miss Hart. "Does anyone have something to share?"

"I was the flower girl at my sister's wedding,"
said Angela.

"That's exciting," said Miss Hart.

Ruby raised her hand halfway. "I was the flower girl at my sister's wedding, too."

"What a coincidence!" said Miss Hart.

Angela turned and smiled at Ruby.

Ruby smiled at the top of Angela's head.

"Class, please take out your reading books," said Miss Hart.

At lunchtime, Ruby hopped all the way home on one foot.

When Ruby came back to school,
she was wearing a red bow in her hair.
She slid into her seat behind Angela.

"I like your bow," whispered Angela.

"I like yours, too," whispered Ruby.

"Class, please take out your math books,"
said Miss Hart.

On Tuesday morning,
Angela wore a sweater with
daisies on it.
    At lunchtime, Ruby
hopped home sideways.

When Ruby came back to school after lunch,
she was wearing a sweater with daisies on it.
"I like your sweater," whispered Angela.
"I like yours, too," whispered Ruby.

On Wednesday, Angela wore a hand-painted
T-shirt with matching sneakers.

After lunch, Ruby hopped back to school wearing
a hand-painted T-shirt with matching sneakers.

"Why are you sitting like that?" whispered Angela.

"Wet paint," said Ruby.

On Thursday morning, during Sharing Time, Angela modeled the flower girl dress she wore at her sister's wedding.

Ruby modeled her flower girl dress, too, right after lunch.

Angela didn't whisper anything.

By coincidence, on Friday morning, both girls
wore red-and-lavender-striped dresses.

At lunchtime, Angela raced home.

When Angela came back to school,
she was wearing black.

On Friday afternoon, Miss Hart asked everyone
to write a short poem.

"Who would like to read first?" asked Miss Hart.

Angela raised her hand. She stood by her desk and read:

I had a cat I could not see,
Because it stayed in back of me.
It was a very loyal pet—
It's sad we never really met.

"That was very good!" said Miss Hart. "Now, who's next?"
Miss Hart looked around the room. "Ruby?"

Ruby stood and recited slowly:

I had a nice pet,
Who I never met,
Because it always stayed behind me.
And I'm sure it was a cat, too.

Ruby smiled at the back of Angela's head.
Someone whispered. Ruby sat down.
"What a coincidence," murmured Miss Hart.

Angela scribbled something on a piece of paper. She passed it to Ruby.

The note said:

YOU COPIED ME!

I'M TELLING MISS HART!

P.S. I HATE YOUR HAIR THAT WAY.

Ruby buried her chin in the collar of her blouse. A big tear rolled down her nose and plopped onto the note.

When the bell rang, Miss Hart sent everyone home except Ruby.

Miss Hart closed the door of the schoolroom
and sat on the edge of Ruby's desk.

"Ruby, dear," she said gently, "you don't need to
copy everything Angela does. You can be anything
you want to be, but be Ruby first. I like Ruby."

Miss Hart smiled at Ruby. Ruby smiled at
Miss Hart's beautiful, polished fingernails.
"Have a nice weekend," said Miss Hart.
"Have a nice weekend," said Ruby.

On Monday morning, Miss Hart said, "I hope everyone had a pleasant weekend. I did! I went to the opera." Miss Hart looked around the room. "Does anyone have something to share?"

Ruby waved her hand. Glued to every finger was a pink plastic fingernail.

"I went to the opera, too!" said Ruby.

"She did not!" whispered Angela.

Miss Hart folded her hands
and looked very serious.

"Ruby, dear," said Miss Hart
gently, "did you do anything else
this weekend?"

Ruby peeled off a fingernail.
"I hopped," said Ruby.

The class giggled.

Ruby's ears turned red.

"But I did! I hopped around the picnic table ten times!" Ruby looked around the room. "Watch!"

Ruby sprang from her desk.

She hopped forward.

She hopped backward.

She hopped sideways with both eyes shut.

The class cheered and clapped their hands
to the beat of Ruby's feet. Ruby was the best
hopper they had ever seen.

Miss Hart turned on the tape player and said,
"Follow the leader! Do the Ruby Hop!"
So Ruby led the class around the room,
while everyone copied *her.*

And at noon, Ruby and Angela hopped home for lunch.

AWARD WINNING
Illustrator

from *Pass It On*

I Can

by Mari Evans
illustrated by Floyd Cooper

I can
be anything
I can
do anything
I can
think
anything
big
or tall
OR
high or low
W I D E
or narrow
fast or slow
because I
CAN
and
I
WANT
TO!

SOURCE

Fantasy

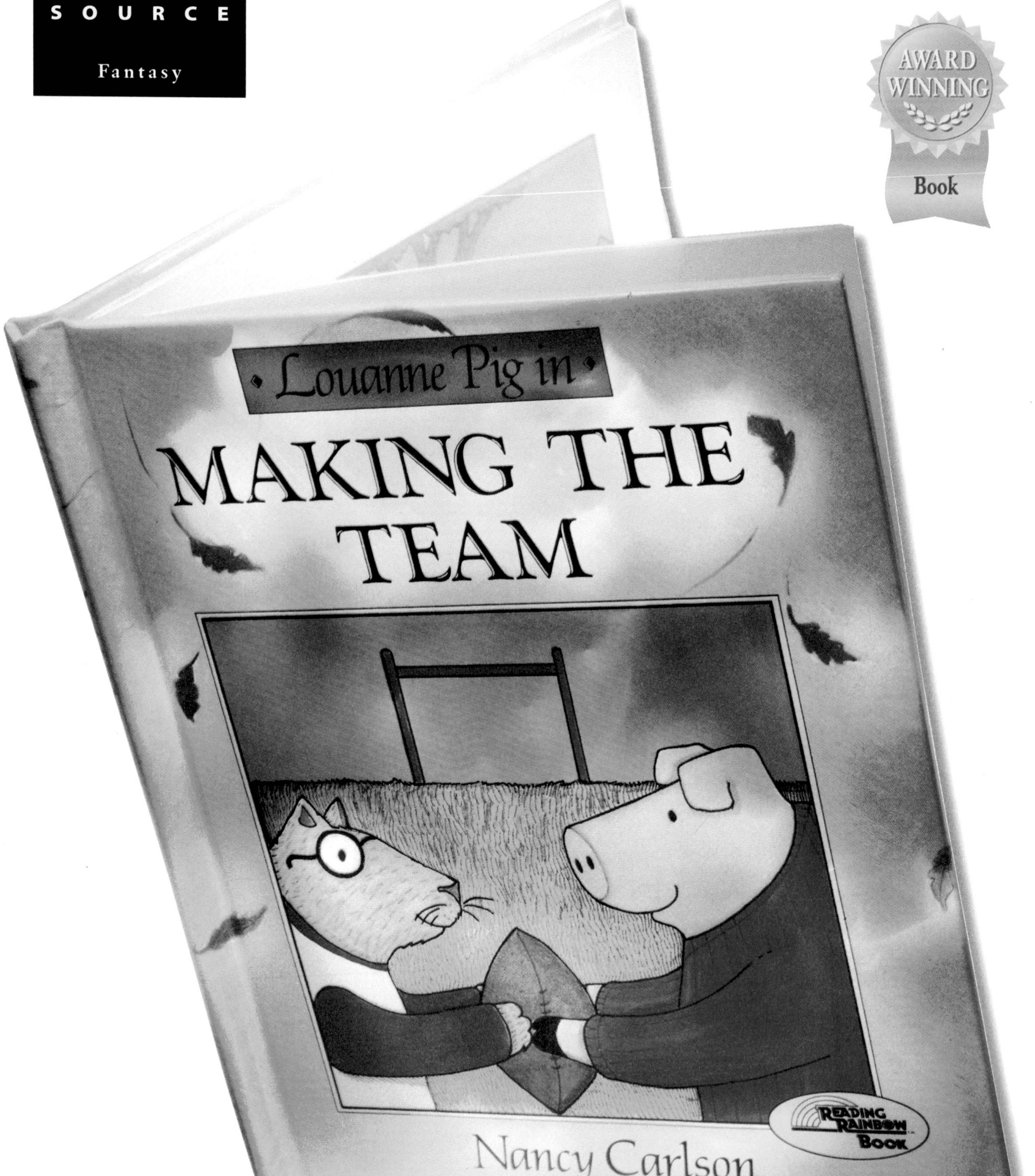
AWARD
WINNING
Book
Louanne Pig in
MAKING THE TEAM
READING RAINBOW BOOK
Nancy Carlson

One day Louanne and Arnie found something exciting on the school bulletin board. Tryouts for the cheerleading squad and the football team were coming up.

"I'm going to try out for cheerleading," said Louanne.

"And I'm going to try out for the football team," said Arnie.

That afternoon they hurried over to Arnie's
to practice together.

Louanne was doing
pretty well...

...until she came to the
split jump. She couldn't get
off the ground.

"Like this, Louanne,"
said Arnie.

"I'm better at cartwheels," said Louanne.

"Let me show you how to do it," said Arnie.

"You ought to be practicing football," said
Louanne, and she picked up the football and
threw it to Arnie.

Arnie missed the catch.

"You have to keep your
eye on the ball, Arnie,"
Louanne told him. "Like this."

"I'm probably better at
tackling," said Arnie.

"Let me show you how to do it," said Louanne.

"Let's try some kicking," said Arnie.

All week long Louanne and Arnie met after school to practice for their tryouts. Louanne's jumps didn't improve much, but Arnie kept her spirits up.

"You really look great!" he told her.

Arnie only rarely caught the ball, but Louanne encouraged him.

"I know you're going to make the team!" she said.

When the big day arrived, their
confidence was high.
Cheerleading tryouts were first.

Louanne didn't make
the squad.

"Don't feel bad," Arnie
consoled her. "There's always
next year. By then you'll be
top-notch."

"Right," said Louanne.
"Come on. There's still
a little time before your
tryout. I'll show you a
few last tricks."

"Hey, pig," said Coach Ed. "You're pretty
good. Why don't you try out for the team."

So Louanne and Arnie tried out together.

Louanne made the team.

Arnie didn't.

Suddenly Louanne had an idea.

"Come on, Arnie!" she said. "Cheerleading tryouts are still going on."

That fall Roosevelt School won every game. Louanne led the team to victory,

and Arnie led the cheers.

MENTOR

Bruce Thorson

Photographer

**Taking pictures is fun.
SNAP that SHOT!**

Have you ever taken a picture of something special to you? Photographers take all kinds of pictures. Good photographers take pictures that show something about themselves.

Bruce Thorson is a photographer. He takes pictures for an Oregon newspaper.

Questions

for Bruce Thorson

Here's how photographer Bruce Thorson shows who he is through his photography.

 **How long have you been taking photographs?**

 I've had a camera since I was nine years old. I've always loved taking pictures.

 What is your job like?

 There's a lot of variety. I drive to a lot of different places. I take pictures of people doing interesting things.

Q What is your favorite thing to photograph?

A Sports. I love football, basketball, and track because there is a lot of action.

Q What do you think your photography tells people about you?

A People say I have an eye for showing what an event was all about. And I guess a lot of my shots show that I love sports!

Bruce Thorson's Tips for Making Pictures

1 Carry a camera or paper and markers wherever you go.

2 Watch an activity for the moment that shows it best.

3 Practice. Make pictures of your friends doing things they like.

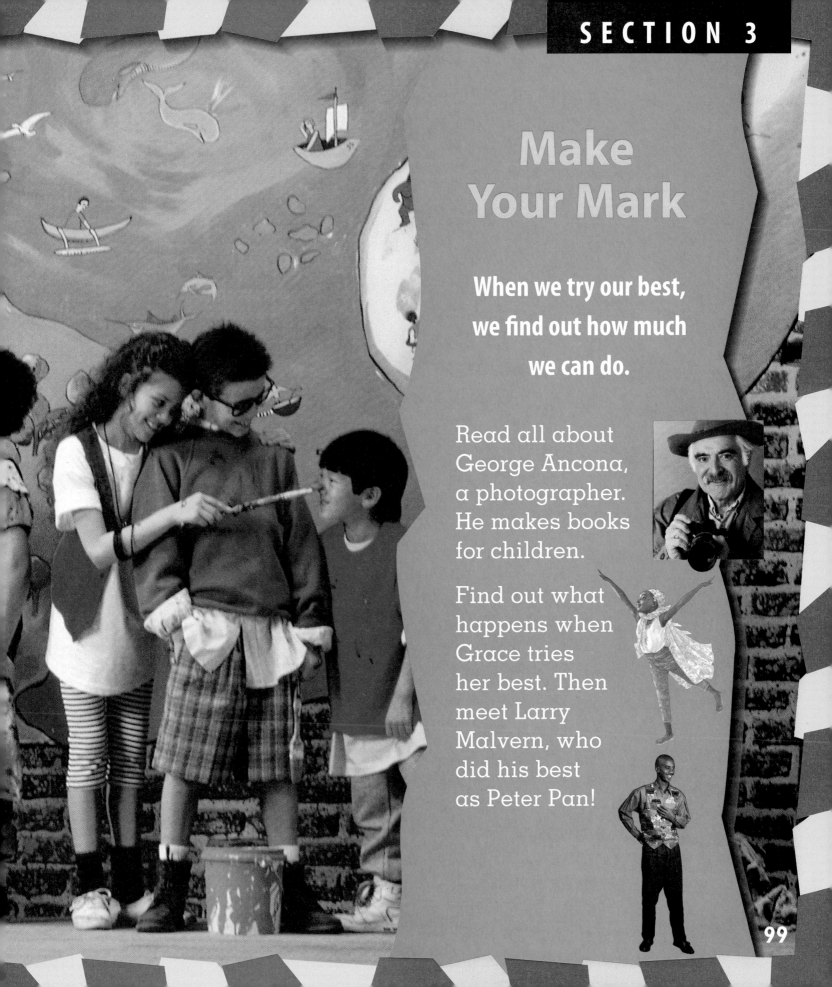

Make Your Mark

When we try our best, we find out how much we can do.

Read all about George Ancona, a photographer. He makes books for children.

Find out what happens when Grace tries her best. Then meet Larry Malvern, who did his best as Peter Pan!

99

GEORGE ANCONA

THEN & NOW

SCHOLASTIC

AWARD WINNING

Author/ Photographer

Mom, Neri, Dad, and me

Me,
4 months old

My parents came to the United States from Mexico before I was born. They spoke only Spanish at home. They named me Jorge (**hor** hay), but they called me Jorgito (hor **hee** to). My friends in school called me Georgie.

◆◇◆

Now I am known as George Ancona.

Mommy and me at Coney Island

My family lived in Coney Island near the beach and the amusement park. When I was little I rode the painted ponies on the merry-go-round. Later, I painted pictures of them. My family would look at my pictures and say, "Jorgito is going to be an artist when he grows up!"

Painted ponies, age 20

Wild mustang, New Mexico

Now I am a photographer.
I look at the world through my camera.

Up to our necks in sand!

A sailor on wheels

Coney Island summer

104

Growing up in Coney Island was exciting.
There was always so much to do and see there.
I loved the sight of the ocean by day and the
bright lights on the rides at night.

I still love to look at the world all around me.

Watching and waiting to take a picture

Dressed for make-believe

As a child, I was always using my imagination. I had an older cousin who gave me the clothes that he outgrew. My favorite things were an aviator helmet and a pair of knee-high boots. Wearing these, I flew make-believe airplanes around my living room.

Now I use my imagination when I take my photographs and write my books.

Click!

Tio Mario, Neri, and me

My uncle, Tio Mario, worked in a sign shop, which I often visited. I loved watching him mix colors in big buckets of paint. He would take a can of yellow, pour in some blue, and mix it. I was amazed when the paint turned green right before my eyes.

Now I'm still amazed when I look through the camera and see something wonderful.

Fancy dancer at Crow Fair, Montana

Dad, me (circled), and the neighbors

My father's hobby was photography.
I explored the city with him on weekends.
We walked along the docks and watched big ships
bringing cargo into the port. While my father
took pictures, I daydreamed about faraway places.
I never thought I would become a photographer, too.

Now I travel all over the world taking photographs
of exciting places.

In a rain forest in Brazil

My grandma,
Chichi Neri

Mérida, diciembre 1° de 1931.
Niño Jorge Efraín Ancona Díaz
New York.

Mi idolatrado hijito:
        El día 4 del presente al cumplir

Letters link my grandma
and me

My first trip to Mexico

When I went to Mexico as a young man,
I met my grandmother for the first time.
She had been writing to me from the day
I was born. Her handwriting was as beautiful
as the things she wrote. Through her letters
she shared her life story with me.

Now I share my life stories with my own children,
grandchildren . . .

My son Pablo and me

Mexico

Honduras

U.S.A.

. . . and children
all over the world.

U.S.A.

Brazil

Honduras

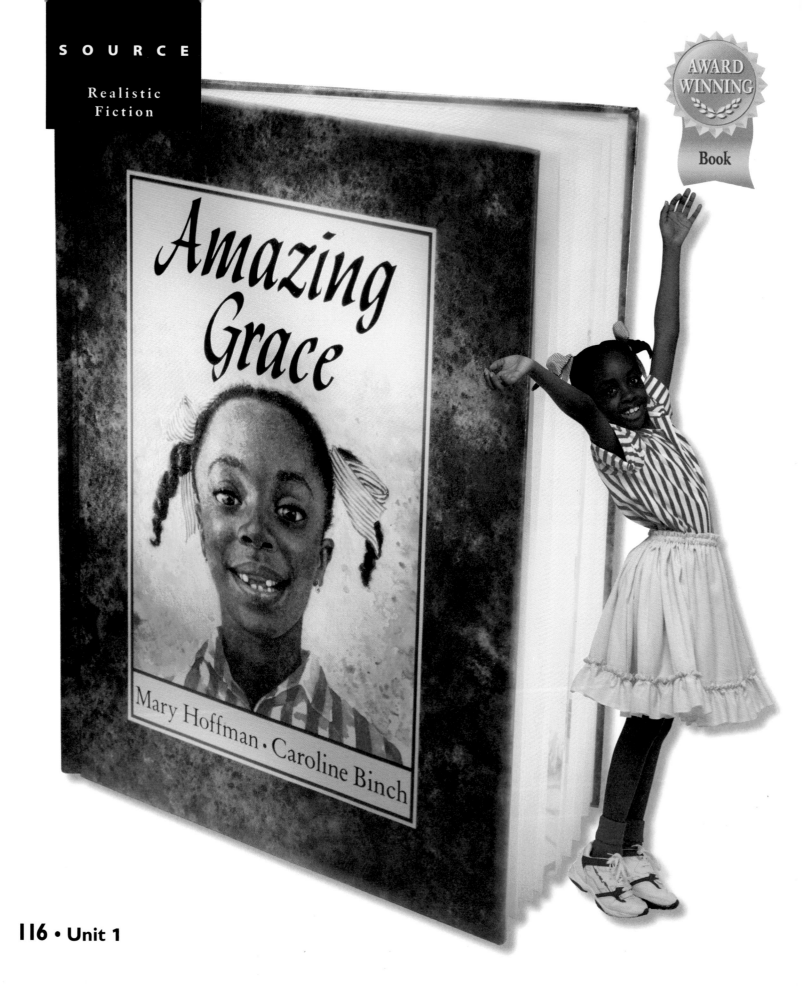

AWARD
WINNING

Book

Amazing
Grace

Mary Hoffman • Caroline Binch

Grace was a girl who loved stories.

She didn't mind if they were read to her or told to her or made up in her own head. She didn't care if they were in books or movies or out of Nana's long memory. Grace just loved stories.

After she had heard them, and sometimes while they were still going on, Grace would act them out. And she always gave herself the most exciting part.

Grace went into battle as Joan of Arc...

and wove a wicked web as Anansi the Spider.

She hid inside the wooden horse at the gates of Troy....

She went exploring for lost kingdoms....

She sailed the seven seas
with a peg leg and a parrot.

She was Hiawatha, sitting by
the shining Big-Sea-Water...

and Mowgli in the backyard jungle.

Most of all Grace loved to act out adventure stories and fairy tales. When there was no one else around, Grace played all the parts herself.

She set out to seek her fortune, with no companion but her trusty cat—and found a city with streets paved in gold.

Or she was Aladdin, rubbing his magic lamp to make the genie appear.

Sometimes she could get Ma and Nana to join in, when they weren't too busy.

Then she was Doctor Grace and their lives were in her hands.

One day Grace's teacher said they would do the play *Peter Pan*. Grace knew who she wanted to be.

When she raised her hand, Raj said, "You can't be Peter—that's a boy's name."

But Grace kept her hand up.

"You can't be Peter Pan," whispered Natalie.
"He isn't black." But Grace kept her hand up.

"All right," said the teacher. "Lots of you want
to be Peter Pan, so we'll have auditions next week
to choose parts." She gave them words to learn.

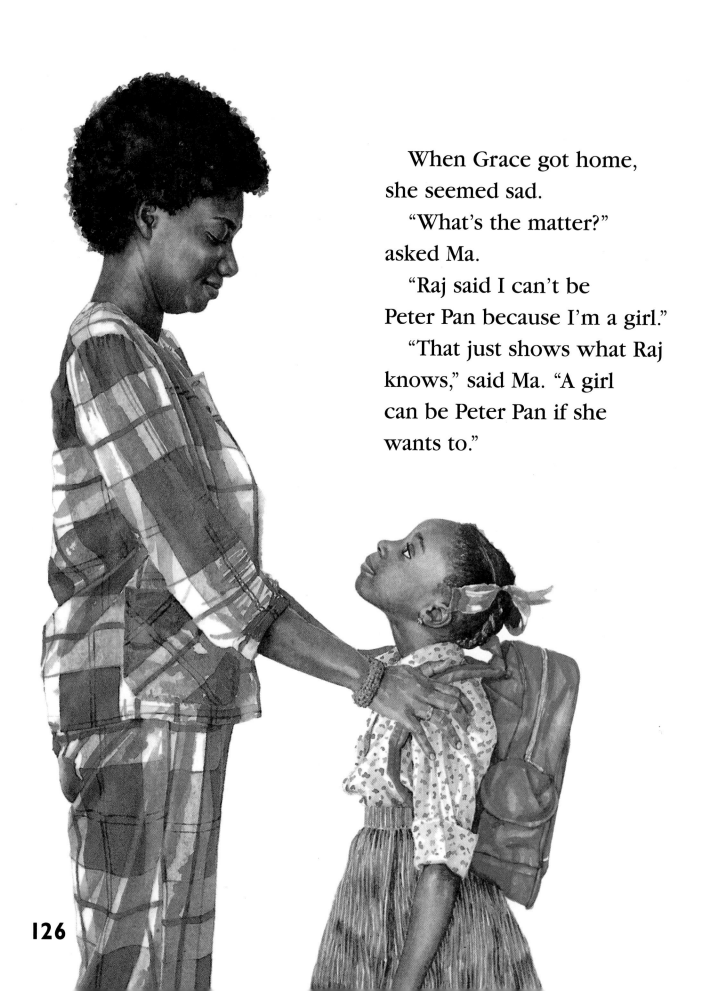

When Grace got home,
she seemed sad.

"What's the matter?"
asked Ma.

"Raj said I can't be
Peter Pan because I'm a girl."

"That just shows what Raj
knows," said Ma. "A girl
can be Peter Pan if she
wants to."

Grace cheered up, then later she remembered something else. "Natalie says I can't be Peter Pan because I'm black," she said.

Ma looked angry. But before she could speak, Nana said, "It seems that Natalie is another one who don't know nothing. You can be anything you want, Grace, if you put your mind to it."

ROSALIE
WILKINS
in
ROMEO & JULIET

ROMEO AND JULIET

ROSALI WILKINS

STUNNING NEW

On Saturday Nana told Grace they were going out. In the afternoon they caught a bus and train into town. Nana took Grace to a grand theater. The sign outside read ROSALIE WILKINS IN *Romeo and Juliet* in sparkling lights.

"Are we going to the ballet, Nana?" asked Grace.

"We are, honey, but first I want you to look at this picture."

Grace looked up and saw a beautiful young ballerina in a tutu. Above the dancer it said STUNNING NEW JULIET.

"That one is little Rosalie from back home in Trinidad," said Nana. "Her granny and me, we grew up together on the island. She's always asking me do I want tickets to see her Rosalie dance—so this time I said yes."

After the ballet Grace played the part of Juliet,
dancing around her room in her imaginary tutu.
I can be anything I want, she thought.

On Monday the class met for auditions to choose who was best for each part.

When it was Grace's turn to be Peter, she knew exactly what to do and all the words to say—she had been Peter Pan all weekend. She took a deep breath and imagined herself flying.

When it was time to vote, the class chose Raj to be Captain Hook and Natalie to be Wendy. There was no doubt who would be Peter Pan. *Everyone* voted for Grace.

"You were fantastic!" whispered Natalie.

The play was a big success and Grace was an amazing Peter Pan.

After it was all over, she said, "I feel as if I could fly all the way home!"

"You probably could," said Ma.

"Yes," said Nana. "If Grace put her mind to it, she can do anything she want."

An Amazing Peter Pan

Larry Malvern was the actor chosen to play Peter Pan when the musical was performed by a theater company in Pennsylvania. Here is a page from the play program and some photographs from the show.

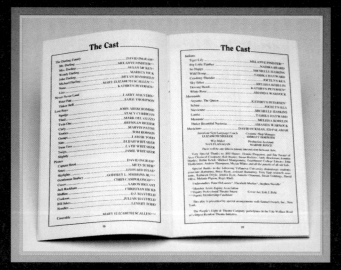

The Cast List

Wendy, Michael, and the Lost Boys

Tinkerbell and Peter Pan

Captain Hook

Glossary

activities
things that you do
Art and swimming are the **activities** I like best.

amazing
surprising
The huge amount of snow in our yard is **amazing**.

announced
said or told
The teacher happily **announced** the date of the play.

artist
a person who creates
The **artist** painted a picture of our school.

auditions
tryouts for a part in a show
He watched the **auditions** for the roles of Jack and Sam in the play.

ballet
a kind of dance
People may dance on their toes when they do **ballet**.

baseball
a game played by two teams with a bat and a ball
In **baseball**, players try to hit the ball with a bat and run around the bases.

ballet

basketball
a game played by two teams trying to throw a large ball through a high hoop

He runs fast and jumps high when he plays **basketball**.

camera
a kind of box used to take pictures or movies

My **camera** takes very good pictures.

clutched
held tightly

She **clutched** the ball when she caught it.

computer
a machine that does many kinds of work very quickly

I wrote a story on a **computer**.

computer

confidence
a strong belief in someone's actions

The teacher had **confidence** that I would pass the test.

crafts
things that are handmade

We saw many beautiful baskets at the **crafts** fair.

camera

139

helmet
a hard hat that protects the head

His **helmet** protected his head when he fell off the bike.

helmet

hobby
something that a person does just for fun

Collecting stamps is a **hobby** many people like.

imaginary
make-believe, not real

The talking animals in the story are **imaginary**.

imagination
the act of creating pictures or ideas in your mind

He used a lot of **imagination** to help him paint pictures.

improve
to make better

If she studies, she can **improve** her grades.

modeled
showed

My friend **modeled** the way to make an airplane.

murmured
spoke in a low, soft voice

I couldn't hear what he said because he **murmured**.

photographer
a person who takes pictures with a camera.

A **photographer** took a picture of my class.

practice
to do something again and again

We **practice** for the class play every day.

recited
said out loud in front of a group

He **recited** his poem in front of the class.

scribbled
wrote quickly or without care

She messily **scribbled** a note as she rushed out of the house.

sneaker
a soft shoe with a flat rubber bottom
The laces on one **sneaker** came untied.

sneaker

soccer
a game played by two teams with a ball that can be moved with every part of the body except the hands
She kicks the ball far when she plays **soccer**.

squad
a small group of people who work together
The police **squad** was getting ready for the parade.

stunning
very beautiful
The queen's costume was **stunning**.

theater
a place to see movies or plays
The **theater** was showing a good movie.

soccer

squad

tiptoed
walked on the toes
She **tiptoed** quietly down the hall.

tryouts
tests to see if a person can do something well
Tryouts for the band are this afternoon.

victory
the act of winning
The captain led our team to **victory**.

whispered
spoke very softly
She **whispered** his name in my ear.

141

Authors and Illustrators

Caroline Binch pages 116-135

Caroline Binch loves to travel. One of her favorite places is Trinidad, the Caribbean island where Grace's family comes from. Binch has worked with author Mary Hoffman on another book about Grace, called *Bountiful Grace.* She also illustrated *Hue Boy* by Rita Mitchell. She wrote and illustrated *Gregory Cool.* Both books are about boys in the Caribbean!

Nancy Carlson pages 76-93

Nancy Carlson likes all kinds of sports—just like her character, Lou Ann. She hopes that her stories will help kids discover that they can do all kinds of things! Her book, *Harriet and the Roller Coaster,* shows why it can be good to try new things. *Arnie and the New Kid* is about two boys who each learn what it means to be a good friend.

Mari Evans page 75

When Mari Evans was in the fourth grade, a story she wrote was published in the school's newspaper. Her father was so proud he told everyone in the family! Knowing that her father believed she had talent made Evans want to keep on writing. Today she is best known for her poems, but she also writes articles, stories, and TV shows.

Patricia Reilly Giff
pages 18-41

Patricia Reilly Giff was a teacher for many years. She began to write stories to make her students laugh. She wanted to tell them they were special. Now she is the author of many books, such as *The Beast in Ms. Rooney's Room.* She wrote another story about Ronald Morgan called *Today Was a Terrible Day.*

SUPER SOLVERS

Tour a
Toy Company

There may be more
than one way to solve
a problem.

3

Clever Ideas

Some problems need clever solutions.

Many Hands

We work together to solve problems.

Try, Try Again

It may take more than one try to solve a problem.

Trade Books

The following books accompany this *Super Solvers* SourceBook.

Illustrator

Humorous Fiction
Miss Nelson Has a Field Day
by Harry Allard
illustrated by James Marshall

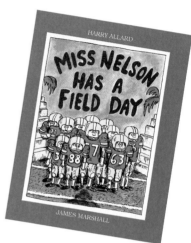

Book

Popular Fiction
Pet Show!
by Ezra Jack Keats

AWARD WINNING
Author/Illustrator

Realistic Fiction
New Shoes for Silvia
by Johanna Hurwitz
illustrated by Jerry Pinkney

Big Book

AWARD WINNING
Book

West African Folk Tale
Zomo the Rabbit
by Gerald McDermott

7

Clever Ideas

Some problems need clever solutions.

Watch a boy solve the problem of having too many **aunts**. Then join a child who's watching **ants** solve their anthill problems.

Be amazed at the way a paper crane helps a restaurant owner with his business.

Meet a toy designer who knows what makes a good toy.

9

Rattigan/Karas

Truman's Aunt Farm

Truman's Aunt Farm

Jama Kim Rattigan

Illustrated by G. Brian Karas

HMCo

AWARD
WINNING

Author

At eleven o'clock a package arrived for Truman. It was a
birthday present from Aunt Fran. Truman looked at the box.
It was not moving. He gently picked it up. It felt empty. He
turned it over, then smelled it. Presents from Aunt Fran had
to be handled very carefully.

Truman slowly opened the box. It was empty! No, there were two cards. The yellow one said: "Happy Birthday dear Truman! I am giving you the ant farm you wanted. Love, your charming Aunt Fran."

The green one said: "Mail this card right away to receive your free ants! Watch them work! Watch them play! Watch them eat! Live ants!"

Truman mailed his card right away. Oh boy. Live ants! Live ants for his very own!

But he didn't get ants. He got *aunts*.

It was true. There were aunts everywhere. They all loved Truman and made such a fuss!

"My, how you've grown," said Aunt Lulu.

"Isn't he handsome?" said Aunt Jodie.

"Looks just like me," said Aunt Ramona. And they hugged him, and patted his head, and pinched his cheeks, and talked his ears off.

Dear Charming Aunt Fran,

Thank you for the birthday present.
I have fifty-something aunts at my house now.
More are arriving daily. What shall I do?

Love,
Your bug-loving nephew, Truman

P.S. What should I feed the aunts?

Truman looked out his front window. A long, long line of aunts was waiting to get in. They brought their knitting and homemade banana bread and gave Truman more than one hundred-something gift subscriptions to children's magazines.

"Help!" yelled Truman.

"Letter for you," said the postman.

My dear Truman,

I am glad you liked the present. Don't let those ants bug you. Do you have any friends who would like some ants?

Love,
Your clever Aunt Fran

P.S. Feed the ants ant food.

Since they were *his* aunts he wanted them to be good aunts. What was the best aunt food? Not coffee, the aunts stayed up all night. Not alphabet soup, the aunts talked too much. Certainly not chocolate, the aunts kissed him all the time.

Daily Schedule

Morning:
9:00 Tickle Practice
10:00 Headstands
10:30 Roller Skating
11:00 Hug Relay

Afternoon:
1:00 Stories
2:00 Naps
3:00 Listening
5:00 Tiptoeing

So Truman fed them rice pudding for breakfast, jelly sandwiches for lunch, and little hot dogs for supper.

Every morning, all the aunts lined up for inspection. Truman walked up and down the ranks. He looked over each aunt from head to toe. They were ready to get to work.

The aunts got water and sun and fresh air. They blew bubbles, flew kites, and found birds' nests. Aunt Amy could do back flips with her eyes closed.

The aunts were strong and happy. They were charming and clever. They slept, played, sang, danced, and talked just enough.

Dear clever Aunt Fran,

I have around two hundred-something aunts now.
I love them all. More aunts keep coming and coming.
They are the best in the world.

Love,
Your aunt-loving nephew, Truman

Yes, they were very good aunts. But they weren't really *his* aunts. And he was running out of room. Could he give them away? Who might want them?

Truman put up a sign:

TRUMAN'S AUNT FARM

LIVE AUNTS!
WATCH THEM WORK!
WATCH THEM PLAY!
WATCH THEM EAT!
FREE TO GOOD HOMES

Truman looked out his front window. A long, long line of boys and girls was waiting to get in.

"I want a funny aunt," said one girl, "one who knows jokes and stories."

"I want my aunt to do cartwheels," said a little boy, "and not cry if she falls down and gets dirty."

"Make mine lumpy and soft. A good cuddler," said another boy.

Truman let all the boys and girls in. They looked over the aunts from head to toe. They watched the aunts work and play. They watched the aunts eat. The aunts could tickle, tell stories, do headstands, and roller skate. When the children talked, the aunts really listened. They didn't pat heads, pinch cheeks, or talk ears off. But they still hugged.

Soon, each child found just the right aunt.

"Goodbye, dear Truman!" called the aunts.

"Thanks for a tiptop time."

Truman was sad to see the aunts go. He watched them tiptoe away. He was glad those boys and girls got their own aunts, but something was missing.

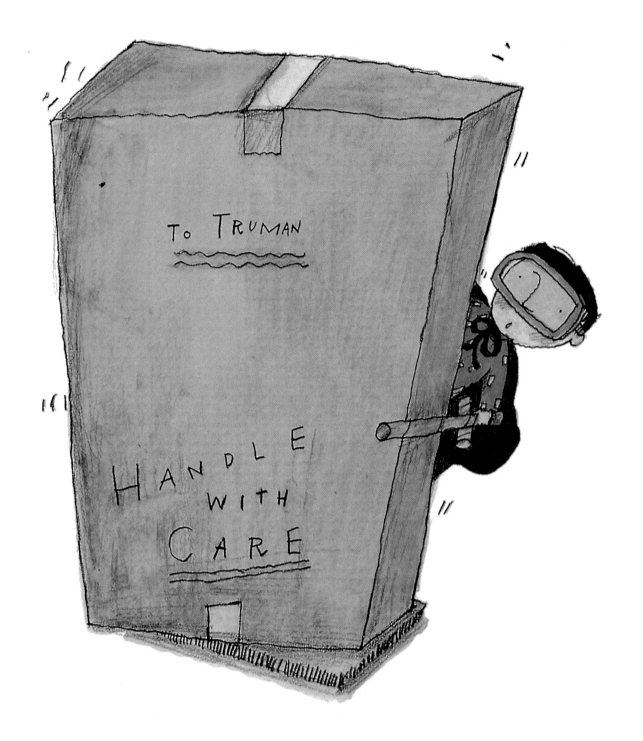

At eleven o'clock the next day another package arrived. Truman looked at the box. It was moving. He tried to pick it up. It was too heavy. He smelled it. It smelled like roses. Carefully, he opened the lid.

Out jumped Aunt Fran!

"Surprise!" She gave Truman a big hug. "But where are your ants?" she said. "I wanted to see them."

"Oh, Aunt Fran! The aunts are gone. They have their own nieces and nephews now."

Aunt Fran put her arm around Truman. He saw the twinkle in her eye. "You did a wonderful thing," said Aunt Fran. "Let's celebrate your birthday."

Truman and his very own Aunt Fran shared a special day.
They had rice pudding for breakfast, jelly sandwiches for
lunch, and little hot dogs for supper. They even had a tickle
contest, but they were too full to do headstands.

Ants

by Mary Ann Hoberman
illustrated by Lisa Adams

I like to watch the ants at work
When I am out at play.
I like to see them run about
And carry crumbs away.

And when I plug an anthill door
To keep them in their den,
I like to see them find a way
To get outside again.

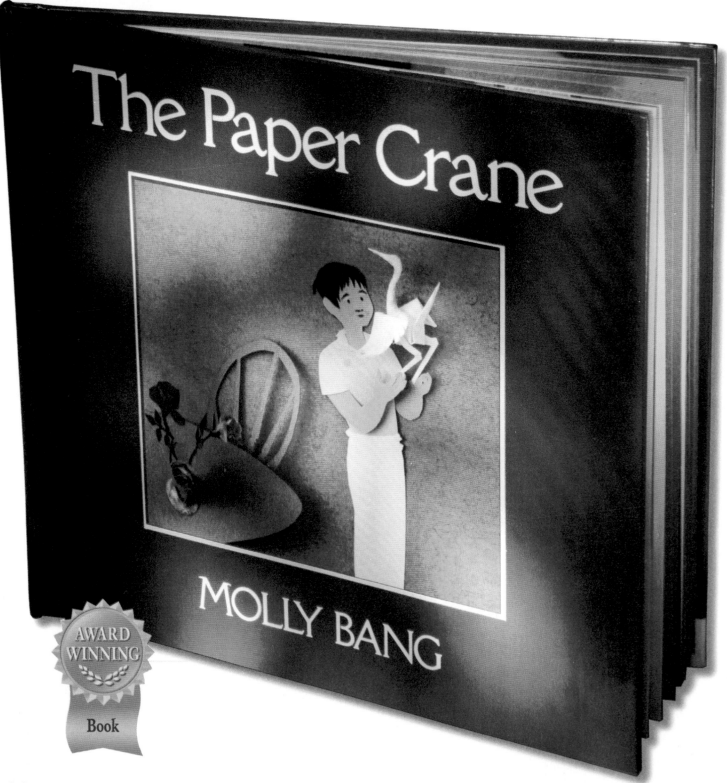

The Paper Crane

MOLLY BANG

A man once owned a restaurant on a busy road.
He loved to cook good food and he loved to serve it.
He worked from morning until night, and he was happy.

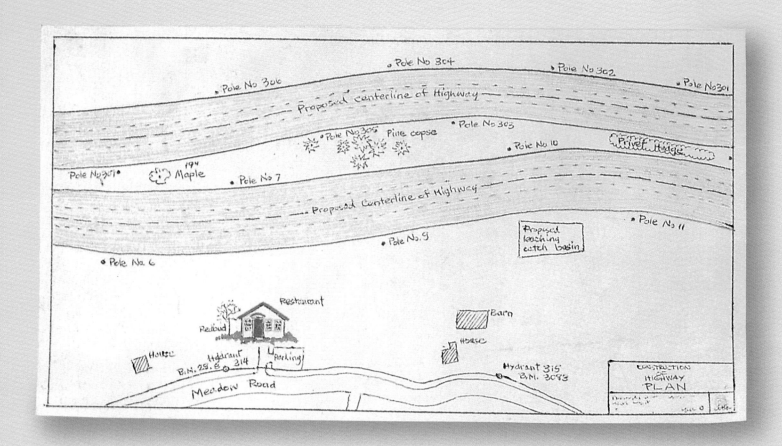

But a new highway was built close by. Travelers drove straight from one place to another and no longer stopped at the restaurant. Many days went by when no guests came at all. The man became very poor, and had nothing to do but dust and polish his empty plates and tables.

One evening a stranger came into the
restaurant. His clothes were old and worn,
but he had an unusual, gentle manner.

Though he said he had no money to pay for food, the owner invited him to sit down. He cooked the best meal he could make and served him like a king.

When the stranger had finished, he said to his host,
"I cannot pay you with money, but I would like to thank
you in my own way."

He picked up a paper napkin from the table and folded it into the shape of a crane. "You have only to clap your hands," he said, "and this bird will come to life and dance for you. Take it, and enjoy it while it is with you." With these words the stranger left.

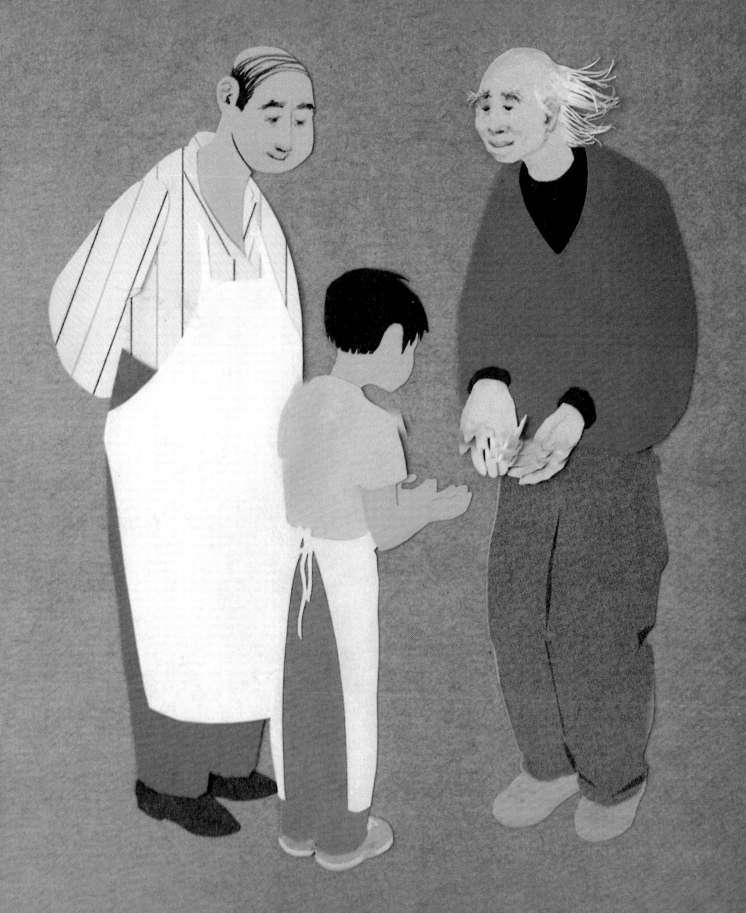

It happened just as the stranger had said. The owner
had only to clap his hands and the paper crane became
a living bird, flew down to the floor, and danced.

Soon word of the dancing crane spread, and people came from far and near to see the magic bird perform. The owner was happy again, for his restaurant was always full of guests.

He cooked and served and had company from morning until night. The weeks passed.   And the months.

One evening a man came into the restaurant. His clothes were old and worn, but he had an unusual, gentle manner. The owner knew him at once and was overjoyed.

The stranger, however, said nothing. He took a flute from his pocket, raised it to his lips, and began to play.

The crane flew down from its place on the shelf and danced as it had never danced before. The stranger finished playing, lowered the flute from his lips, and returned it to his pocket. He climbed on the back of the crane, and they flew out of the door and away.

48

The restaurant still stands by the side of the road, and guests still come to eat the good food and hear the story of the gentle stranger and the magic crane made from a paper napkin. But neither the stranger nor the dancing crane has ever been seen again.

MENTOR

Mary Rodas

Toy Designer

A toy that's NOT fun?
That's a PROBLEM!

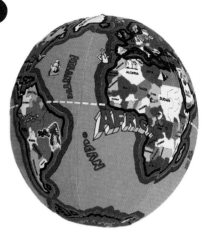

Some people just love problems! Finding and fixing problems are part of some people's jobs.

Mary Rodas is the vice president of Catco Inc., a toy company. When the company makes a toy, Rodas's job is to look at it and see if there is any problem. She works on the toy to make sure it's fun!

52

Questions

Here's how toy designer Mary Rodas solves problems on her job.

Q **How did you get this job while you were still in school?**

A When my neighbor Donald Spector started inventing toys, he would ask me what I thought of his new toy ideas. When he started his own toy company, he hired me to help him.

Q **How do you decide if a toy might have a problem?**

A First, a designer shows me a drawing of a new toy. Then, I look at a model of it. I try to think if the toy will be fun for children. If not, it should be changed.

Q Have you solved a problem about a toy?

A One day I was looking at a white ball called a Balzac Balloon Ball®. I thought the color wasn't exciting, so the designers made the ball in bright colors. Now the ball is a big hit!

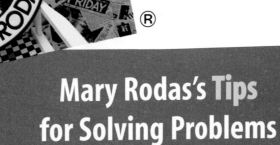

Mary Rodas's Tips for Solving Problems

1 Be positive. Believe you can solve the problem.

2 Don't give up. Keep trying ways to find a solution.

3 If you need help, don't be afraid to ask for it.

55

Many Hands

We work together to solve problems.

Find out how a boy gets some very messy pigs to clean up.

Join a group of mice as they figure out how to save themselves from the cat. Then read the advice children give to other children.

SOURCE

Fantasy

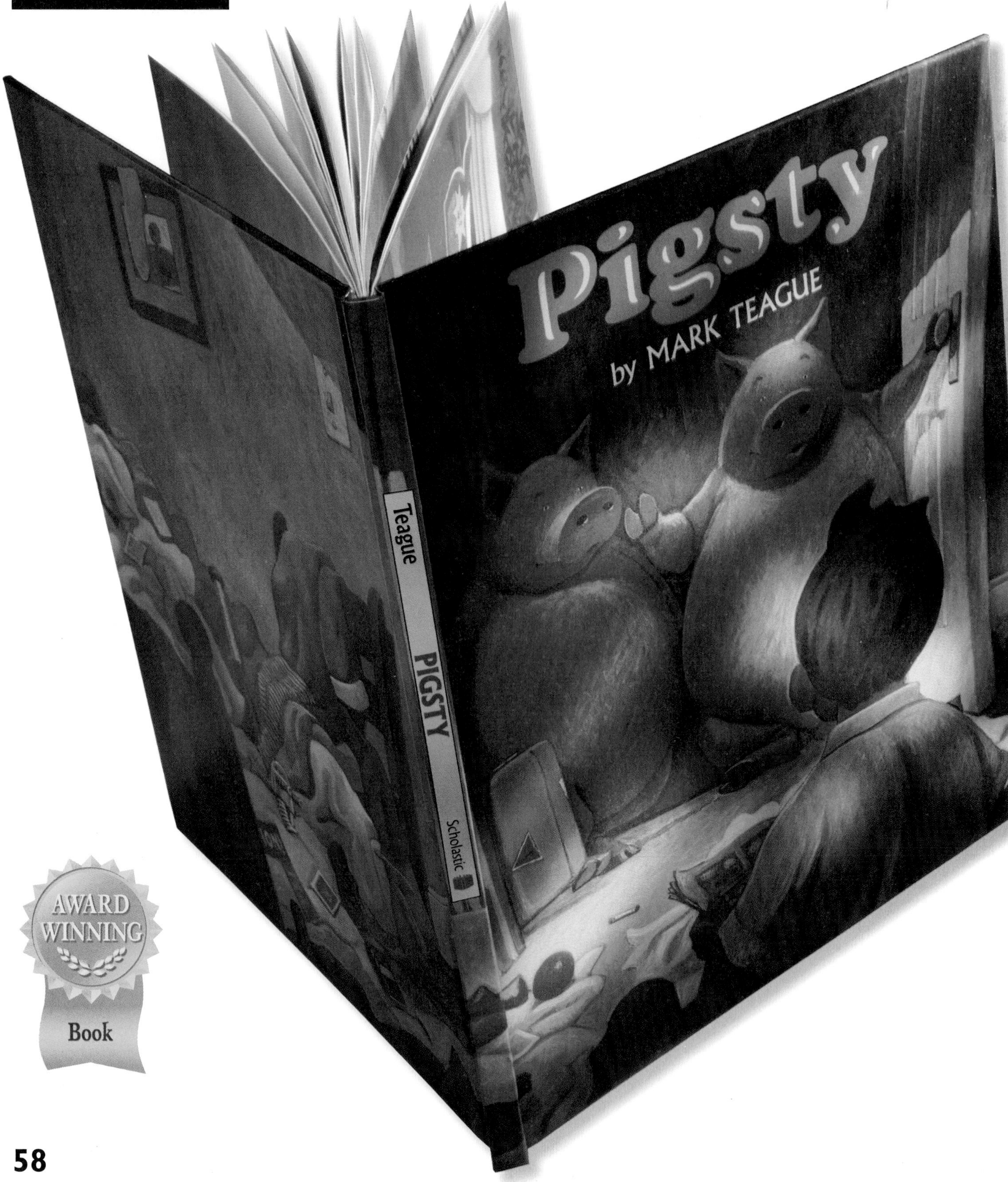
Pigsty
by MARK TEAGUE
Teague
PIGSTY
Scholastic

AWARD WINNING Book

onday afternoon Wendell Fultz's
mother told him to clean his room.
"It's turning into a pigsty," she said.

Wendell went upstairs. Much to his surprise,
a large pig was sitting on his bed.

"Pardon me," said Wendell. He shoved some toys into his closet. But the pig didn't seem to mind the mess, and Wendell found that he didn't mind the pig, either.

He decided to take a break.

When Wendell's mother came to look at his
room, the pig was hiding, but the mess was
still there. She threw up her hands.

"Okay, Wendell," she said. "If you want
to live in a pigsty, that's up to you."

Wendell could hardly believe his luck. "Now I can live however I want."

He didn't even worry when he came home on Tuesday and found a second pig in his room. The mess had grown a bit worse, but he was able to jam most of it under his bed.

"Pigs are all right," he said, "as long as it's only one or two."

In fact, they had a wonderful time. They played Monopoly
until late each night . . .

. . . and left the pieces lying all over the floor.

They had paper airplane wars and pillow fights.
The bed became a trampoline.

Then two more pigs showed up.
The mess just grew and grew.

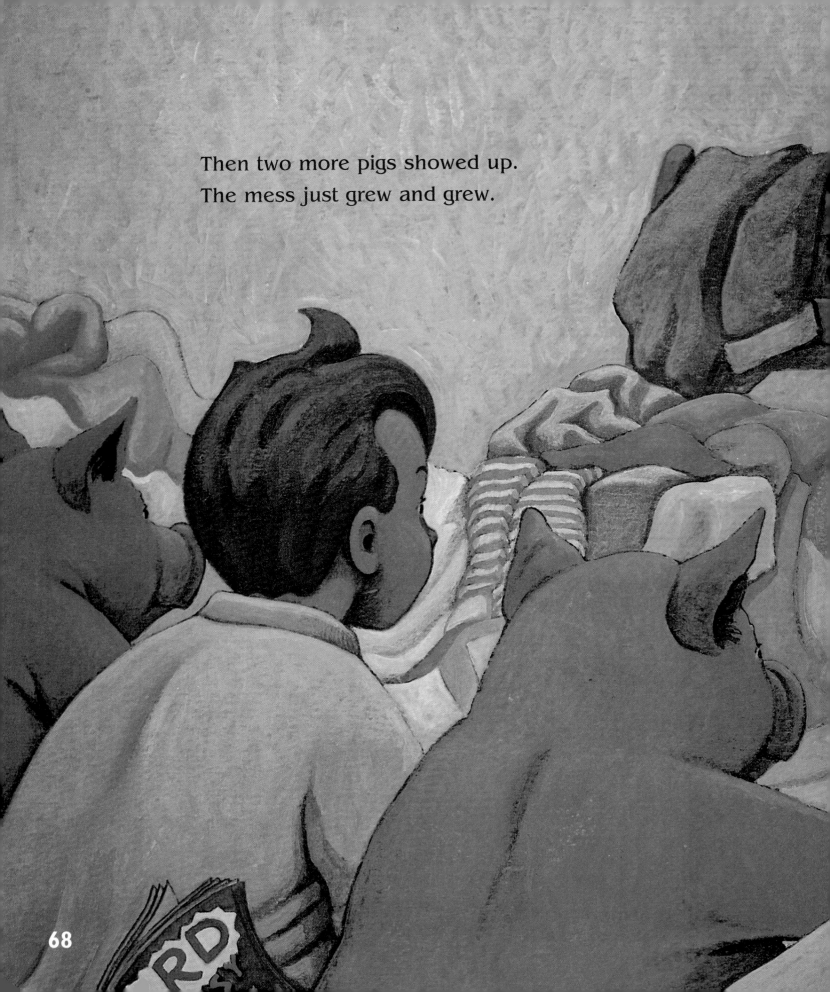

That night when Wendell went to bed, the pigs were lying everywhere. They rolled up in his blankets and hogged his pillows, too.

Wendell told himself he didn't mind, but then he found hoofprints on his comic books.

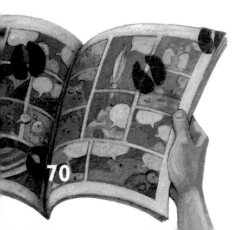

And Friday when he got home from school, he saw
that someone had been sitting on his basketball.
And his baseball cards were chewed.

"That does it!" said Wendell. "I've had enough!"
He ran downstairs to tell his mother.

"Sorry," she said, "but your room is your
responsibility." She handed him a broom.

72

Wendell started to complain. The mess was too huge. But suddenly he remembered a saying he'd heard, that "many hooves make light work."

He marched upstairs and organized a cleaning crew.

They swept and scoured, polished and scrubbed.

Later that afternoon, Wendell inspected his room
and pronounced it "clean."

In fact, it was a bit too clean, from a pig's point of view. So while Wendell inspected, the pigs prepared to go home. One of them made a phone call, and a farm truck came to pick them up. They hugged and grunted and oinked "good-bye."

From that day on, Wendell kept his room clean . . .

. . . except for those nights
when his friends came by
to play Monopoly.

from

ONCE IN A WOOD
TEN TALES FROM AESOP

Adapted and illustrated by
Eve Rice

BELLING THE CAT

A hungry cat had come to stay
and all the mice lived in fear.
The mice decided
they would call a meeting.

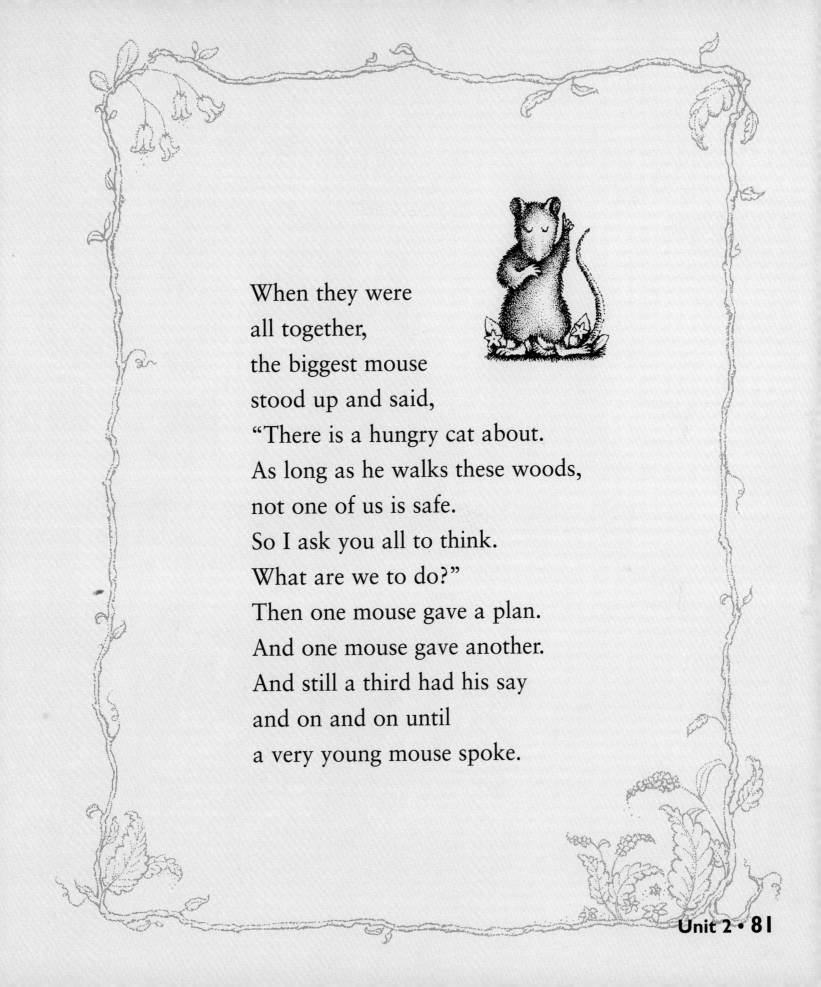

When they were
all together,
the biggest mouse
stood up and said,
"There is a hungry cat about.
As long as he walks these woods,
not one of us is safe.
So I ask you all to think.
What are we to do?"
Then one mouse gave a plan.
And one mouse gave another.
And still a third had his say
and on and on until
a very young mouse spoke.

"Friends," he said.
"I think that we can
solve this problem easily:

Hang a bell on the cat.
Then we will know when he is near
and we can stay out of his way."

"A good idea!" someone called.
And all the other mice agreed.
"We'll be safe at last!" they said
and danced around until
a very old mouse spoke.

"Friends," he said.
"One moment, please.
Things are easier said than done—
the old and wise will tell you that.
So now, will someone tell me this:
Who is going to bell the cat?"

Friends

Photos by Julie Bidwell
Illustration by Maja Anderson

Dear Kids,
  I have a big problem.
I don't have any friends
at my new school. I
don't know what to say
to other kids, so most
of them think I'm stuck
up. When I try to join
them at recess, they
just walk away. No one
likes me, and I can't
stand it. What should
I do?

　　　　Jessica B.
　　　　Texas

We asked our Kids Helping Kids panel about Jessica's letter. Here are the panel's ideas.

JESSE
Maybe the kids are a little shy around someone new. Maybe there's another new person at school you could get to know first.

ADAM
Keep asking to play. They will let you.

86

ANDREA

Ask yourself why you are so scared. You know that you're new there, and you can't expect to get to know kids right away.

MICHAEL

Find something to do by yourself, like jump rope. Someone may want to join you after all.

KA'LISHA

If they walk away from you, just let it go. Making friends takes time.

YEISSMAN

Joining a club will help you get to know other kids, and they'll get to know you, too.

When the Sitter
JUST SITS

Dear Kids,
Please help. My baby sitter never spends any time with me. She picks me up and brings me home. Then she sends me upstairs to do my homework. Then she plops down on the couch and watches TV or talks on the phone. When my homework is all done, she never wants to do anything fun. What can I do?

Sean
California

JESSE

You should talk to her and ask why she doesn't want to do anything fun. Maybe you could change the schedule to make time for things she'll enjoy doing with you. She may want to help with your homework if you ask her. Maybe you could ask the sitter to come up with ideas to help pass the time.

MICHAEL

Your mother is paying her to keep you company. If she doesn't, then tell your mother what's going on. I don't think she'll want to lose her job. Make the TV off-limits for everyone.

ANDREA

Maybe there are games she'd like to play if you ask her. Maybe you can go over to a friend's house to play or ride a bike. Or you can ask your parents for another sitter because this one just isn't interested in you.

ADAM

Ask your parents for permission to watch TV after your homework is done. Tell your parents that you want to watch your TV shows, not just the ones the sitter likes.

YEISSMAN

Talk to the sitter and tell her you want to do something fun. If that doesn't work, just keep trying. Tell her you're bored and you need something to do. Maybe your parents have some ideas to make the time more fun for both of you.

KA'LISHA

Find something to do on your own. You have rights, too. See if you can play with your friends when the sitter is there. Maybe you and the sitter can cook together.

Try, Try Again

It may take more than one try to solve a problem.

Break codes to read secret messages from the Code King. Then meet the man who created the art for this story.

Take notes with Martí as he tries to figure out what a mango is. See how many ways a chicken finds to share her fruit.

THE CODE KING

by Bill Dallas Lewis

SCHOLASTIC

It was a slow Saturday afternoon, and Rosa and
Jimmy were sitting at the bus stop with nothing to do.
"I'm bored," Jimmy said.
"We could go to a movie," suggested Rosa.
The Main Street bus pulled up. Some people got on
and the bus pulled away.

Just then, a paper airplane landed at Jimmy's feet. He picked it up and unfolded it. There was writing inside.

"What does that mean?" asked Jimmy.

"It must be a secret code," said Rosa.

Jimmy took a pencil from his pocket. Then he drew lines between some letters. "I've got it!" he said. "It's lots of words stuck together. In the park, under the slide, is a great place for a clue to hide!"

96

Rosa and Jimmy ran to the neighborhood park.
"There's the note," Jimmy yelled.
They studied the piece of paper.

"I like pizza with extra cheese, pepperoni, and mushrooms, please. This is easy now," said Rosa. "Maybe we can catch up with the Code King at Higgy's Pizza Place!"

When Rosa and Jimmy got to Higgy's, they sat down at the counter and looked around.

Mrs. Higgy came up to them. "Hi, kids," she said, "someone left this note for you."

Rosa opened the note and looked at it.

F R F R S V T E A
I E I E A E H D Y

C P A N O E S W B O K A A
A T I R G R T O L C S W Y

THE CODE KING

"Hmmmmm," Jimmy said. "The Code King has changed his code."

"What if we zigzag the letters up and down?" asked Rosa. "Hand me that pencil, Jimmy."

Suddenly Rosa called out, "Fire. Fire. Save the day. Captain Rogers, two blocks away."

HELP THE MAN THEY CALL POP
HE HAS A LIST FOR YOU TO SHOP
THE CODE KING♛

100

Captain Rogers was polishing his fire engine when Jimmy and Rosa arrived at the fire station. "Hi," Jimmy said. "Did anyone leave a message for us?"

Captain Rogers pointed to the chalkboard and said, "Look there."

They looked at the message on the chalkboard for a long time. They were about to give up. Then Jimmy called out, "Rosa! Look at the reflection on the truck! Now the message makes sense. The words on the chalkboard were written backwards."

HELP THE MAN THEY CALL POP
HE HAS A LIST FOR YOU TO SHOP
THE CODE KING

"They call my neighbor, Mr. Jones, Pop. I know where he lives. Follow me!" Jimmy said.

Jimmy and Rosa raced to Mr. Jones's house. Rosa knocked on the door.

"Hi. Here's the list," said Mr. Jones. He handed over a piece of paper and some money. "Thanks for doing my shopping," he said.

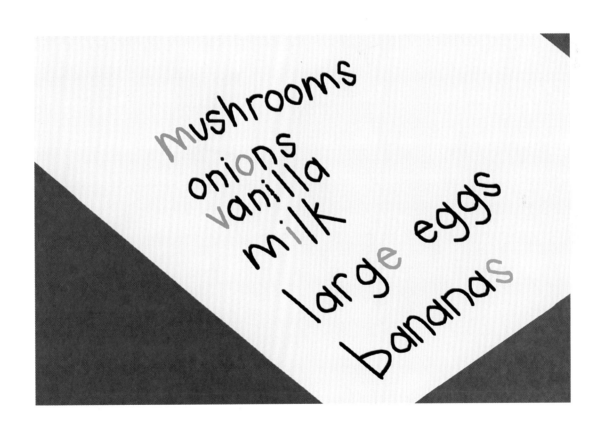

104

At the Sunflower Market, Jimmy and Rosa bought all the items on the list. Then they returned to see Mr. Jones.

"Here's your list back," Rosa said after handing over the groceries.

"Keep the list," said Mr. Jones. "There's a message on the back for you."

Rosa turned the paper over and read it.

When Jimmy and Rosa looked at the shopping list this time, they noticed that each word had one letter in green. When they put the green letters together, they spelled "movies."

Outside the movie theater, Rosa said, "I don't see any
Code King, do you?"

"No," Jimmy answered glumly. "And no more clues, either."

Rosa tugged Jimmy's sleeve. "There's your sister, Tina!"

Tina walked over and said, "Hi. I have three tickets for the
next movie. Want to go?"

Jimmy asked, "How did you know we would be here?"

Tina smiled and said, "The Code King has her ways."

Secrets of THE CODE KING Artist: Bill Dallas Lewis

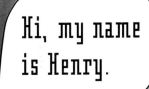

Hi, my name is Henry.

Why do you like to use the computer to draw?

"My computer's name is Henry. He is my second-best friend in the world. Using Henry, I can make big changes in my pictures. When you use crayons or watercolors, you can't do that. I can change day to night in a picture by pushing one button."

How do you make people on the computer?

"I use something special called a curve tool. I make a big circle for the head. I make little circles for the eyes. Then I make different curves for the mouth, nose, ears, arms, and legs. The curve tool is great for making hair too!"

How do you make the same person over and over again?

"Once I draw a person I save her in Henry's memory. When I need to use her again, I pull her up out of Henry's memory. If she needs to be bigger for the new picture, I can stretch her. I can bend her arms or change a smile to a frown."

Martí lived on a small island, in a tiny house, at the base of a very tall tree.

Martí was a simple mouse, whose life consisted of simple pleasures: spending time with his best friend Gomez, afternoons in the sun, and a good imported Swiss cheese every now and again.

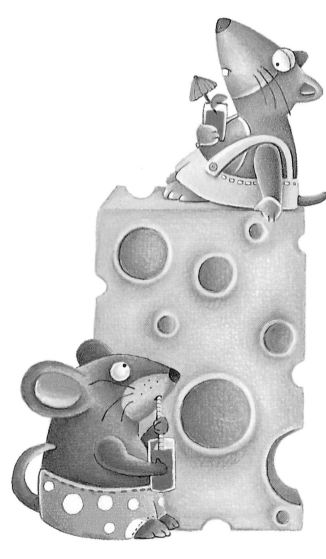

One day, however, Martí was faced with a rather extraordinary task.

He awoke as usual, and, as usual, he did his morning exercises. But when he went outside, he found a note from his friend Gomez tacked to the front of his door.

Dinner Tonight at my house. Bring a mango. —Gomez

"A mango?" thought Martí. "Who ever heard of such a thing? What does a mango look like?" he wondered. "And where on earth can I get one?"

Martí was a very curious mouse.

uickly, Martí put on his lucky shirt and headed out in search of this mysterious mango. First he decided to stop next door at the lily pond, where his neighbor Frog was on his way out.

"Excuse me," said Martí.
"What's a mango?"

"A mango is a fruit!" Frog said, and—KERPLUNK—disappeared into the pond.

"Now we're getting somewhere," thought Martí. He took out his notebook and made a note that a mango is a fruit, and went on.

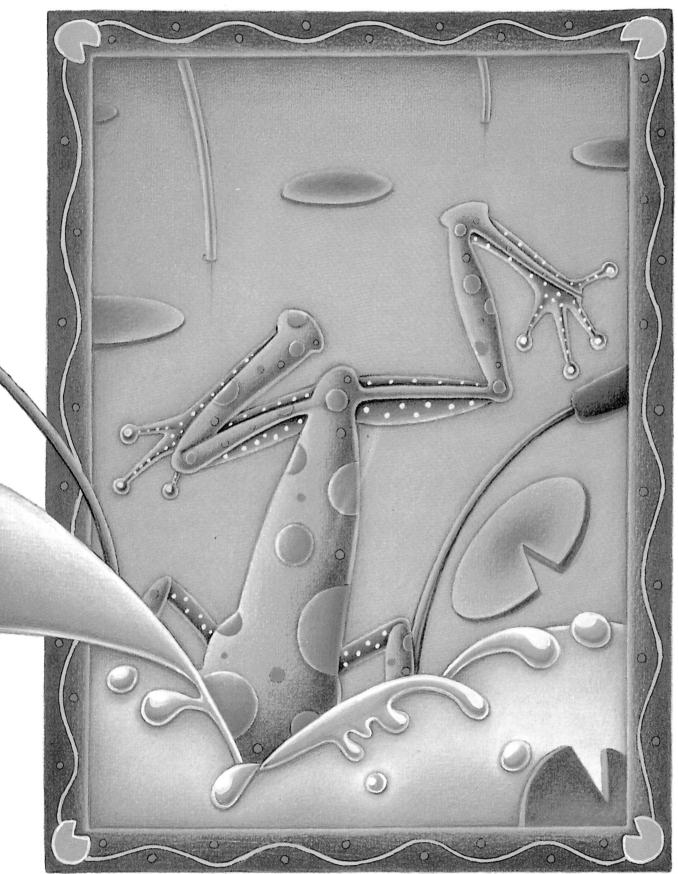

econd, Martí came across a gorilla gathering guavas.

"Excuse me," said Martí, "are those mangos?"

"Of course not," groaned the gorilla. "Mangos are much bigger. These are guavas."

"Thank you," said Martí. He made a note that a mango is a fruit bigger than a guava, and went on.

Next, he met a worm working her way through a watermelon.

"Excuse me," said Martí, "is that a mango?"

"Not to my knowledge," whispered the worm. "A mango is much smaller. This is a watermelon."

"Thank you," said Martí. He made a note that a mango is a fruit bigger than a guava, but smaller than a watermelon, and went on.

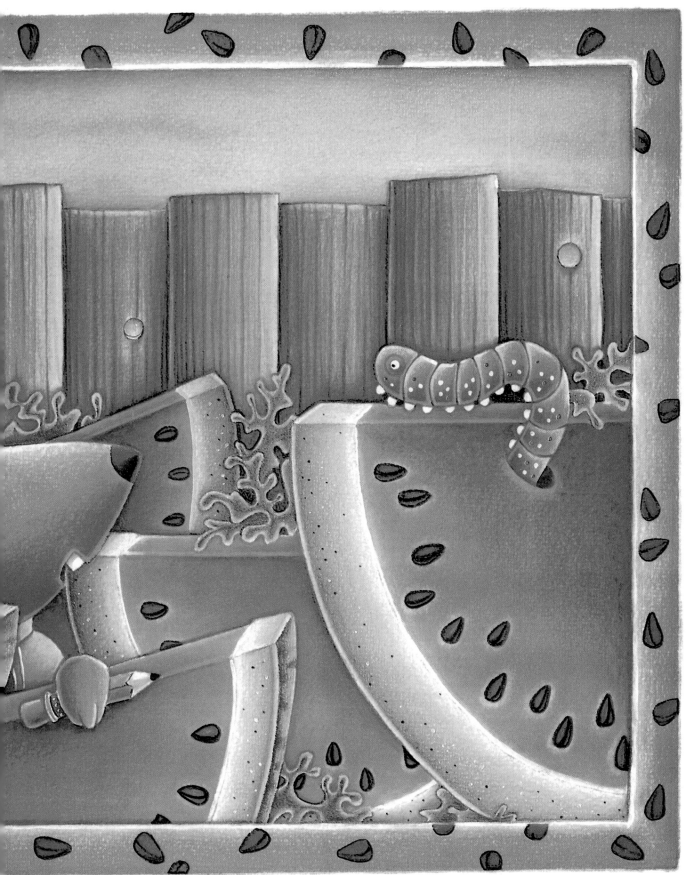

oon after, Martí saw a kangaroo collecting kiwis.

"Excuse me," said Martí, "are those mangos?"

"Not at all," crooned the kangaroo. "Mangos are much smoother. These are kiwis."

"Thank you," said Martí. He made a note that a mango is a fruit bigger than a guava, but smaller than a watermelon, and smoother than a kiwi, and went on.

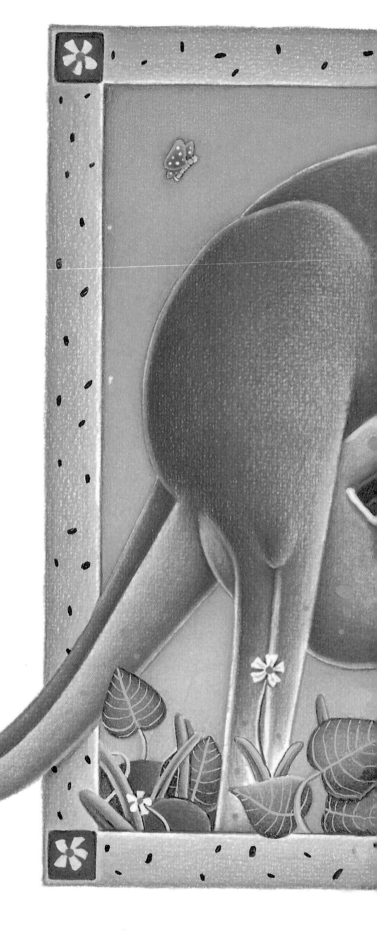

Later, Martí ran into some beavers bearing bananas.

"Excuse me," said Martí, "are those mangos?"

"No, no, no," babbled a beaver. "Mangos are much rounder. These are bananas."

"Thank you," said Martí. He made a note that a mango is a fruit bigger than a guava, but smaller than a watermelon, smoother than a kiwi, and rounder than a banana, and went on.

In the afternoon, Martí came upon a cockroach creeping across a coconut.

"Excuse me," said Martí, "is that a mango?"

"Hardly!" croaked the cockroach. "A mango is much softer. This is a coconut."

"Thank you," said Martí. He made a note that a mango is a fruit bigger than a guava, but smaller than a watermelon, smoother than a kiwi, rounder than a banana, and softer than a coconut, and went on.

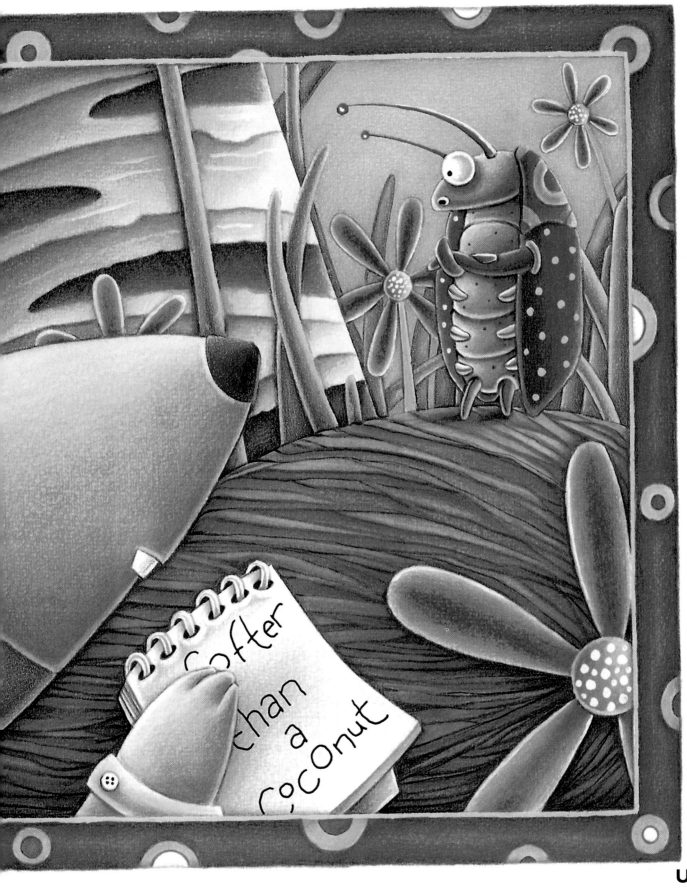

Then he came to an alligator arranging some avocados.

"Excuse me," said Martí, "are those mangos?"

But the alligator did not answer. So Martí went on.

124

By now it was getting late, and Martí had become quite discouraged. He decided to head home without his mango. When he got there, he sat down, tired from his search.

"I'll never find this mango," said Martí unhappily. "I can't find anything. I can't go to Gomez's party without a mango. I'm a failure."

Martí was a very depressed mouse.

Just then Frog came bouncing by on a fig.
"I see you've found your mango," he said to Martí.

"Please don't tease me," begged Martí. "I have
not found my mango."

"But you're sitting right on
it!" bellowed Frog, and he
bounced off down the hill.

Martí looked down to see just what it was he was sitting on. "Could this be a mango?" he thought. He referred to his notes.

a mango is a fruit

Bigger than a guava

Smaller than a Watermelon

Smoother than a kiwi

Rounder than a Banana

Softer than a Coconut

"This *is* a mango!" cheered Martí. And he smiled a very big smile.

Martí was a very happy mouse.

from Fraction Action

A Fair Share

by Loreen Leedy

One Saturday at about noon, Sadie heard a loud knock at the door.

134

136

Glossary

agreed
said yes
to something
The teacher **agreed**
to take us to the zoo
next week.

avocados
fruits shaped like
pears, but with green
or black skin and
yellow-green insides
Avocados can be
cut up in slices
for a salad.

avocado

cards
folded pieces of paper
with a greeting
for a special day
My sister got a lot of
cards on her birthday.

celebrate
to show happiness
by doing something
special
My family had a party
to **celebrate** my
brother's new job.

clothes
things that we wear
Jamal's favorite
clothes are a blue
T-shirt and jeans.

clue
something that helps
you solve a mystery
or know what
happened
The food on the
baby's face was a
clue that he had just
eaten lunch.

code
a secret way of
writing in which
letters or numbers
have a special
meaning
Tanya and her best
friend write notes
to each other in a
special **code**.

company
people in a group
Most people like **company** when they go on a trip.

decided
chose after thinking about something
The class **decided** to present a play to the whole school.

gift
something special given to someone
The bicycle was the best **gift** she had ever gotten.

guavas
yellow or green fruits often shaped like pears, with white or pink insides
Guavas can be used to make jelly.

guavas

guests
people who are visiting someone's home or staying at a hotel
Ryan and his brother are **guests** at our house for the holidays.

host
a person who greets people in a restaurant
The **host** seated the people at a table in the corner.

idea
a thought
I have an **idea** for something to do Saturday afternoon.

kiwis
small fruits shaped like eggs, with brown fuzzy skin and green insides
After we peeled the **kiwis**, we put them in the salad.

kiwis

mango
a fruit that has tough skin with a rosy tint and orange insides
A **mango** is a juicy fruit.

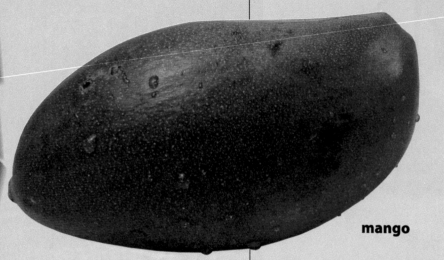

mango

message
news sent from one person to another
Denise sent a **message** to her friend Trisha.

package
a box with something in it
He opened the biggest **package** first.

pigsty
a messy, dirty place like a pen for pigs
If she doesn't clean her room soon, it will turn into a **pigsty**.

polished
made bright and shiny
Eric **polished** his shoes until they shined.

present
something given for a special reason
He brought a **present** to his friend's party.

restaurant
a place where people buy and eat meals
Pat and Dave ate dinner at that **restaurant**.

scoured
cleaned by rubbing with something rough
I **scoured** the pan with a pad to get it clean.

scrubbed
cleaned by rubbing hard
I **scrubbed** the bathtub with a soapy brush.

secret
something that is hidden or not known by many people
We had a **secret** that we never told anyone.

solve
to find the answer
Can you **solve** this puzzle?

stranger
someone you don't know
Don't go anywhere with a **stranger**.

surprise
something you don't know about before it happens
We jumped from our hiding places as a **surprise** when Uncle Joe walked in.

swept
cleaned with a broom
I **swept** all the broken pieces off the floor.

travelers
people who visit another place
The **travelers** are tired from their long trip.

watermelon
a large fruit with green skin and red insides
We cut the huge **watermelon** into thick slices.

wise
makes good decisions, knows a lot
Our grandmother is very **wise** about bringing up children.

zigzag
a line that looks like a *Z* or one *Z* after another
The football player ran a **zigzag** across the field.

watermelons

Authors and Illustrators

Molly Bang pages 32–51

When Molly Bang worked on *The Paper Crane*, she tried many ways of making the pictures until she found the best way. She cut out colored pieces of construction paper and glued them onto paper. It took her a whole year to make all the pictures! Some other books she has written and illustrated are *Ten, Nine, Eight* and *Yellow Ball*.

Loreen Leedy pages 132–137

Reading, writing, and art have been Loreen Leedy's three favorite things since she was a little girl. Working on picture books is the perfect job for her! Many of Leedy's books use funny animal characters to show all the steps in real-life events. *The Furry News* explains how a newspaper works. *The Great Trash Bash* tells how a town cleans up.

Daniel Moreton
pages 108–131

Daniel Moreton says that his character Martí isn't just any mouse. Martí is a Cuban mouse! He is named after a famous Cuban hero. Because the author's family comes from Cuba, he wanted some Cuban things in his first story. The book is filled with pictures that show what Cuba is like.

Mark Teague   pages 58–79

Mark Teague used to work in a bookstore. Looking at the children's books got him thinking about doing his own. Strange and funny things are always happening in books by Teague. In *The Trouble With the Johnsons*, a boy moves in with a family of alligators. In *Frog Medicine*, a boy's book report leads him to visit a doctor who is a frog!

Lights!
Camera!
Action!

Have Fun at

a Children's Theater

Creative teams produce great performances.

Strike Up the Band

We come together to put on a performance.

Cast and Crew

Performances combine the talents of many people.

5

Showtime!

Clear plans and directions help team members create projects.

6

Trade Books

The following books accompany this *Lights! Camera! Action!* SourceBook.

Humorous Fiction
Baseball Ballerina
by Kathryn Cristaldi
illustrated by Abby Carter

Fantasy
Sheep Dreams
by Arthur A. Levine
illustrated by Judy Lanfredi

Realistic Fiction
Song and Dance Man Caldecott Award
by Karen Ackerman
illustrated by
Stephen Gammell

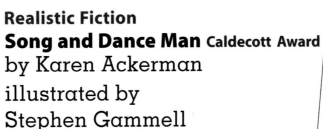

Big Book

Fantasy
The Bunny Play
by Loreen Leedy

Strike Up the Band

We come together to put on a performance.

Watch the unusual show four animals put on for some robbers.

Join in the music celebration in two different communities.

The Bremen Town
Musicians

by HANS WILHELM

AWARD
WINNING

Author/
Illustrator

There was once a donkey
whose master made him carry sacks
to the mill year after year.
Now the donkey was getting old,
and his strength began to fail.

When the master realized that the donkey
was of no use to him anymore,
he decided to get rid of him.
But the donkey guessed
that something bad was in the wind,
so he made up his mind to run away.

He thought he would take the road to Bremen,
where he might get an engagement as a town musician.

On the way,
he found a dog lying by the side of the road,
panting as if he had been running for a long time.
"Now, Holdfast, why are you so out of breath?"
asked the donkey.

"Oh, dear!" said the dog. "I am old and getting weaker
every day, and I can no longer hunt.
My master was going to kill me, but I escaped!
Now how am I to make a living?"

"I will tell you what," said the donkey.
"I am going to Bremen to become a town musician.
Come with me. I can play the lute,
and you can beat the drum."

The dog liked the idea, and they walked on together.

It was not long before they came to a cat sitting by
the roadside, looking as dismal as three wet days.
"Now then, what is the matter with you, old Whiskerwiper?"
asked the donkey.

"Who can be cheerful when his life is in danger?"
answered the cat. "Now that I am old, my teeth are getting blunt,
and I'd rather sit by the fire than chase after mice.
Because of this, my mistress wanted to drown me,
so I ran away. But now I don't know what is
to become of me."

"Come with us to Bremen," said the donkey,
"and be a town musician. You know how to serenade."

The cat liked the idea and went along with them.

Soon the three runaways passed by a yard.
A rooster was perched on top of the gate,
crowing as loudly as he could.
"Your cries are breaking my heart," said the donkey.
"What is the matter?"

"Tomorrow is Sunday and I have foretold good weather,"
said the rooster, "but my mistress is expecting guests
and has ordered the cook to cut off my head
and put me in the soup.
Therefore, I cry with all my might
while I still can."

"You'd better come along with us, Redhead," the donkey said.
"We are going to Bremen to become town musicians.
We could do with a powerful voice like yours."

This sounded perfect to the rooster, so all four went on together.

But Bremen was too far to be reached in one day.
Towards evening they came to a forest
where they decided to spend the night.

The donkey and the dog lay down under a huge tree,
the cat found a place among the branches,
and the rooster flew up to the top of the tree where he felt safe.
But before he went to sleep, the rooster looked all around
to the four points of the compass.
Suddenly he saw a small light shining in the distance.

He called out to his friends,
"There must be a house over there."

"Let's go and see," said the donkey,
"for this place is not very comfortable."

"And there might be
a few bones," said the dog.

They all set off in the direction of the light.
It grew larger and larger until it led them
to a robber's house, all lighted up.

The donkey—who was the tallest—
went to the window and looked in.
"Well, what do you see?" asked the dog.

"What do I see?" answered the donkey.
"I see a table loaded with wonderful
things to eat and to drink. And
robbers are sitting around the table,
having a great time!"

"That would be perfect for us!"
said the rooster.

"Yes, indeed," replied the donkey.
"I wish we were there."

The four friends put their heads together
to decide how they might scare off the robbers.
Finally they knew what to do.

The donkey placed his forefeet on the windowsill.
The dog got on the donkey's back,
the cat stood on the top of the dog, and lastly,
the rooster flew up and perched
on the cat's head.

24

At a given signal, they all
began to perform their music.
The donkey brayed,
the dog barked,
the cat meowed,
and the rooster crowed!

Then they burst into the room,
breaking the windowpanes.
The robbers fled at the dreadful noise.
They thought it was some goblin
and ran to the forest in the utmost terror.

The four friends sat down at the table
and feasted as if they hadn't eaten for weeks.
When they had finished they put out the lights
and looked for places to sleep.
The donkey found a comfortable spot outside,
the dog lay down behind the door,
the cat curled up on the hearth by the warm ashes,
and the rooster settled himself in the loft.
And since they were all very tired from their long journey,
they soon fell asleep.

In the forest, from a safe distance away,
the robbers were watching the house the whole time.
Shortly after midnight they saw that no light was burning
and that everything appeared peaceful.

"We shouldn't have been such cowards and run away!"
said their leader, and he ordered one of them to go back
and check out the house.

The robber went into the house and found everything very quiet.

He went into the kitchen to strike a light, and the cat woke up.
Thinking that the cat's glowing eyes were burning coals,
the robber held a match to them in order to light it.
The cat did not find this funny. He flew into the robber's
face, spitting and scratching.

The robber screamed in terror
and ran to get out through
the back door. But the dog,
who was lying there, leaped up
and bit the robber's leg.

The frightened robber rushed into
the yard where the donkey
struck out and gave him
a great kick with his hind foot.

And the rooster,
who had been wakened
by the noise, cried his loudest,
"Kee-ka-ree-kee!"

The robber ran back to the others
as fast as he could,
and said, "Oh, dear!
In that house there is a gruesome witch.
I felt her breath, and she scratched me
with her long nails.
And by the door there stands a monster
who stabbed me in the leg with a knife.
And in the yard there lies a fierce giant
who beat me with a club.
And on the roof
there sits a judge
who cried, 'Bring the thief to me!'
I got out of that place as fast as I could!"

This scared the robbers so much that they never
went back to that house again.

And the four musicians liked their new home
so much that they stayed forever
and never went to Bremen Town at all.

AWARD
WINNING
Book

Our big chair often sits in our living room empty now.

When I first got my accordion, Grandma and Mama used to sit in that chair together to listen to me practice. And every day after school while Mama was at her job at the diner, Grandma would be sitting in the chair by the window. Even if it was snowing big flakes down on her hair, she would lean way out to call, "Hurry up, Pussycat. I've got something nice for you."

But now Grandma is sick. She has to stay upstairs in the big bed in Aunt Ida and Uncle Sandy's extra room. Mama and Aunt Ida and Uncle Sandy and I take turns taking care of her. When I come home from school, I run right upstairs to ask Grandma if she wants anything. I carry up the soup Mama has left for her. I water her plants and report if the Christmas cactus has any flowers yet. Then I sit on her bed and tell her about everything.

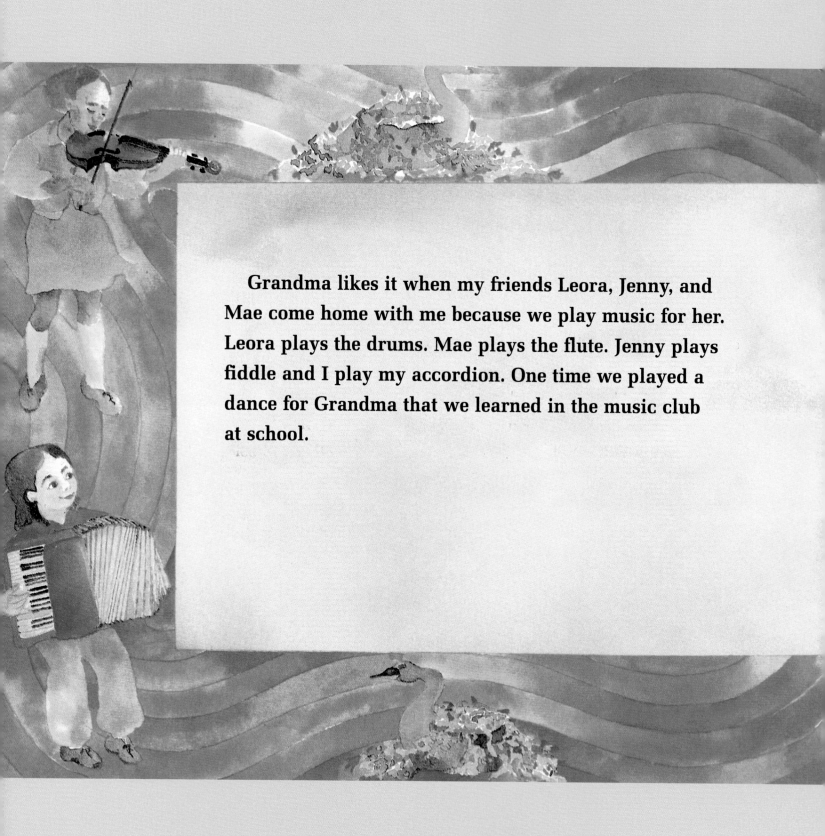

Grandma likes it when my friends Leora, Jenny, and Mae come home with me because we play music for her. Leora plays the drums. Mae plays the flute. Jenny plays fiddle and I play my accordion. One time we played a dance for Grandma that we learned in the music club at school.

Grandma clapped until it made her too tired. She told us it was like the music in the village where she lived when she was a girl. It made her want to dance right down the street. We had to keep her from trying to hop out of bed to go to the kitchen to fix us a treat.

Leora and Jenny and Mae and I left Grandma to rest and went down to get our own treat. We squeezed together into our big chair to eat it.

44

"It feels sad down here without your grandma," Leora said. "Even your big money jar up there looks sad and empty."

"Remember how it was full to the top and I couldn't even lift it when we bought the chair for my mother?" I said.

"And remember how it was more than half full when you got your accordion?" Jenny said.

"I bet it's empty now because your mother has to spend all her money to take care of your grandma till she gets better. That's how it was when my father had his accident and couldn't go to work for a long time," Mae said.

Mae had a dime in her pocket and she dropped it into the jar. "That will make it look a little fuller anyway," she said as she went home.

46

But after Jenny and Leora and Mae went home, our jar looked even emptier to me. I wondered how we would ever be able to fill it up again while Grandma was sick. I wondered when Grandma would be able to come downstairs again. Even our beautiful chair with roses all over it seemed empty with just me in the corner of it. The whole house seemed so empty and so quiet.

I got out my accordion and I started to play. The notes sounded beautiful in the empty room. One song that is an old tune sounded so pretty I played it over and over. I remembered what my mother had told me about my other grandma and how she used to play the accordion. Even when she was a girl not much bigger than I, she would get up and play at a party or a wedding so the company could dance and sing. Then people would stamp their feet and yell, "More, more!" When they went home, they would leave money on the table for her.

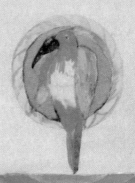

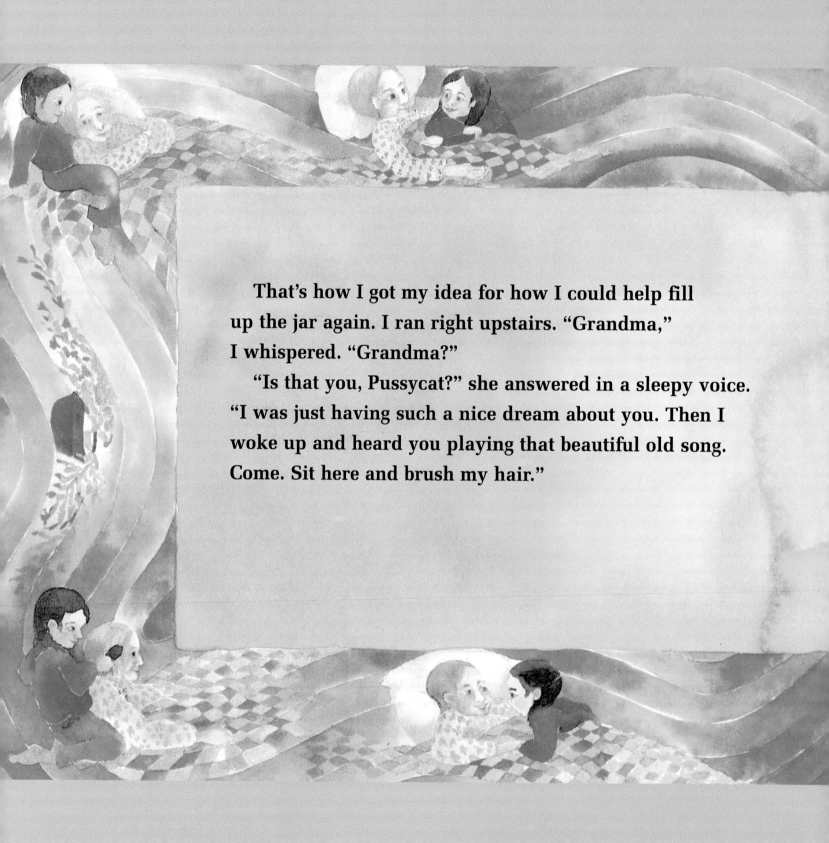

That's how I got my idea for how I could help fill
up the jar again. I ran right upstairs. "Grandma,"
I whispered. "Grandma?"

"Is that you, Pussycat?" she answered in a sleepy voice.
"I was just having such a nice dream about you. Then I
woke up and heard you playing that beautiful old song.
Come. Sit here and brush my hair."

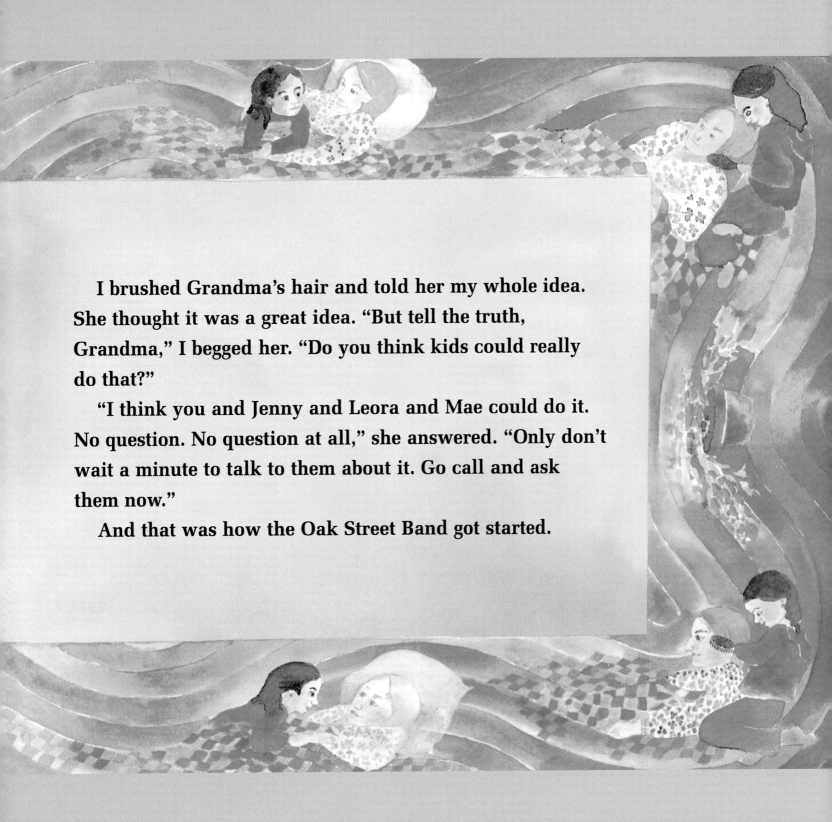

I brushed Grandma's hair and told her my whole idea. She thought it was a great idea. "But tell the truth, Grandma," I begged her. "Do you think kids could really do that?"

"I think you and Jenny and Leora and Mae could do it. No question. No question at all," she answered. "Only don't wait a minute to talk to them about it. Go call and ask them now."

And that was how the Oak Street Band got started.

Our music teachers helped us pick out pieces we could all play together. Aunt Ida, who plays guitar, helped us practice. We practiced on our back porch. One day our neighbor leaned out his window in his pajamas and yelled, "Listen, kids, you sound great but give me a break. I work at night. I've got to get some sleep in the daytime." After that we practiced inside. Grandma said it was helping her get better faster than anything.

At last my accordion teacher said we sounded very good. Uncle Sandy said so too. Aunt Ida and Grandma said we were terrific. Mama said she thought anyone would be glad to have us play for them.

It was Leora's mother who gave us our first job. She asked us to come and play at a party for Leora's great-grandmother and great-grandfather. It was going to be a special anniversary for them. It was fifty years ago on that day they first opened their market on our corner. Now Leora's mother takes care of the market. She always plays the radio loud while she works. But for the party she said there just had to be live music.

All of Leora's aunts and uncles and cousins came to the party. Lots of people from our block came too. Mama and Aunt Ida and Uncle Sandy walked down from our house very slowly with Grandma. It was Grandma's first big day out.

There was a long table in the backyard made from little tables all pushed together. It was covered with so many big dishes of food you could hardly see the tablecloth. But I was too excited to eat anything.

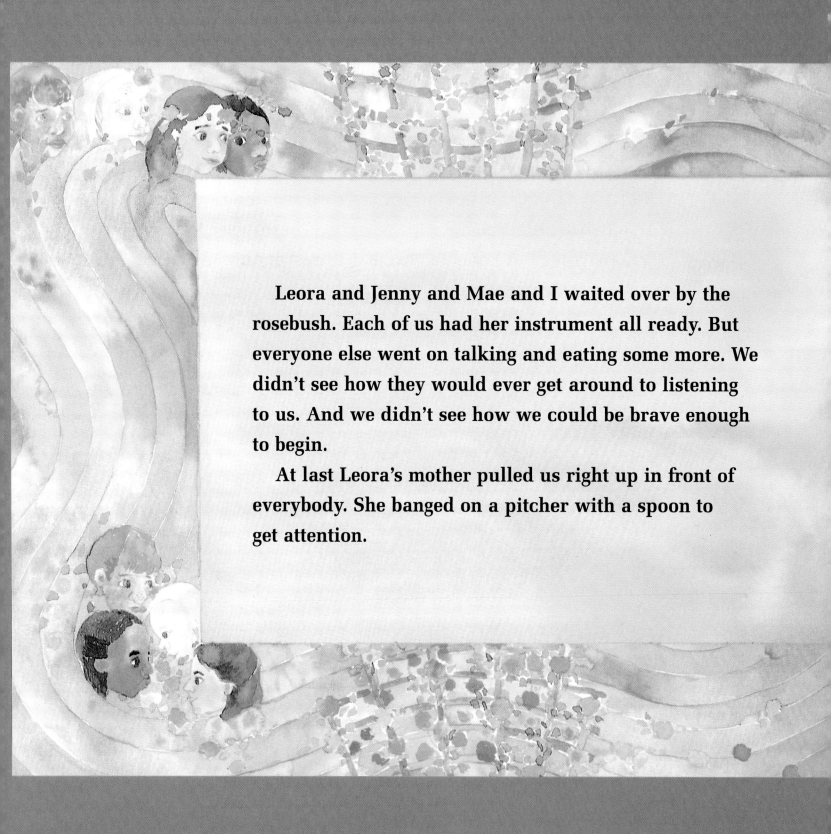

Leora and Jenny and Mae and I waited over by the rosebush. Each of us had her instrument all ready. But everyone else went on talking and eating some more. We didn't see how they would ever get around to listening to us. And we didn't see how we could be brave enough to begin.

At last Leora's mother pulled us right up in front of everybody. She banged on a pitcher with a spoon to get attention.

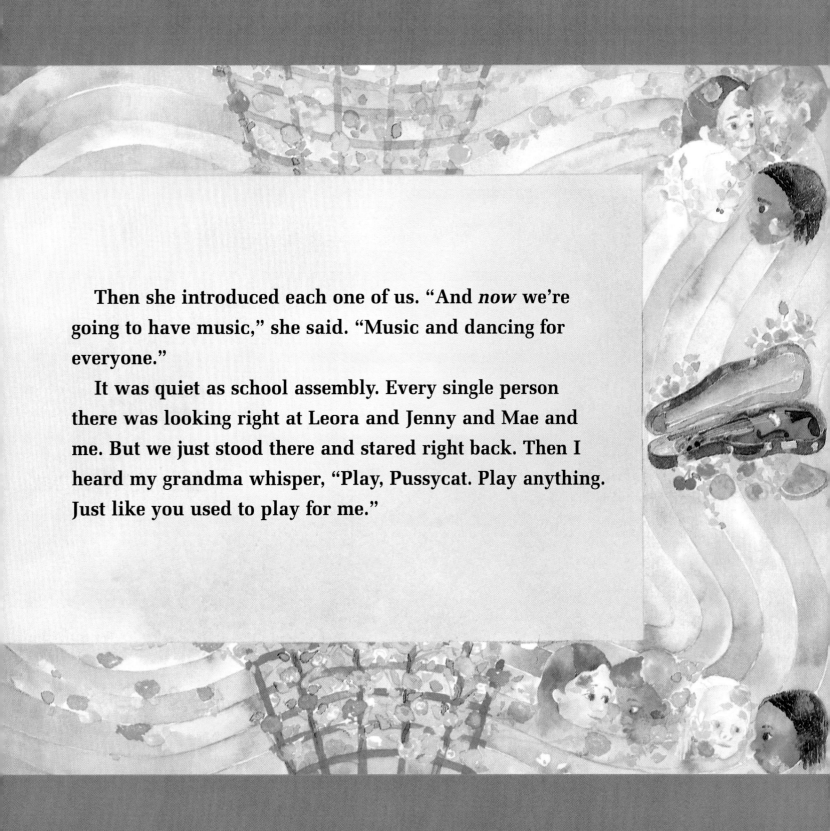

Then she introduced each one of us. "And *now* we're going to have music," she said. "Music and dancing for everyone."

It was quiet as school assembly. Every single person there was looking right at Leora and Jenny and Mae and me. But we just stood there and stared right back. Then I heard my grandma whisper, "Play, Pussycat. Play anything. Just like you used to play for me."

I put my fingers on the keys and buttons of my accordion. Jenny tucked her fiddle under her chin. Mae put her flute to her mouth. Leora held up her drums. After that we played and played. We made mistakes, but we played like a real band. The little lanterns came on. Everyone danced.

Mama and Aunt Ida and Uncle Sandy smiled at us every time they danced by. Grandma kept time nodding her head and tapping with the cane she uses now. Leora and Jenny and Mae and I forgot about being scared. We loved the sound of the Oak Street Band.

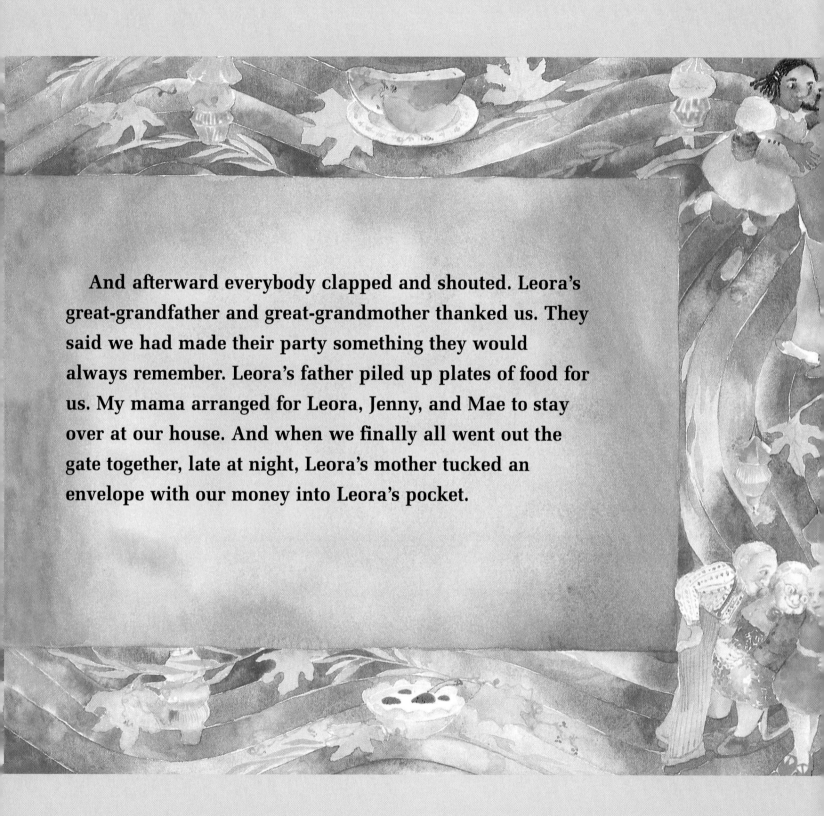

And afterward everybody clapped and shouted. Leora's great-grandfather and great-grandmother thanked us. They said we had made their party something they would always remember. Leora's father piled up plates of food for us. My mama arranged for Leora, Jenny, and Mae to stay over at our house. And when we finally all went out the gate together, late at night, Leora's mother tucked an envelope with our money into Leora's pocket.

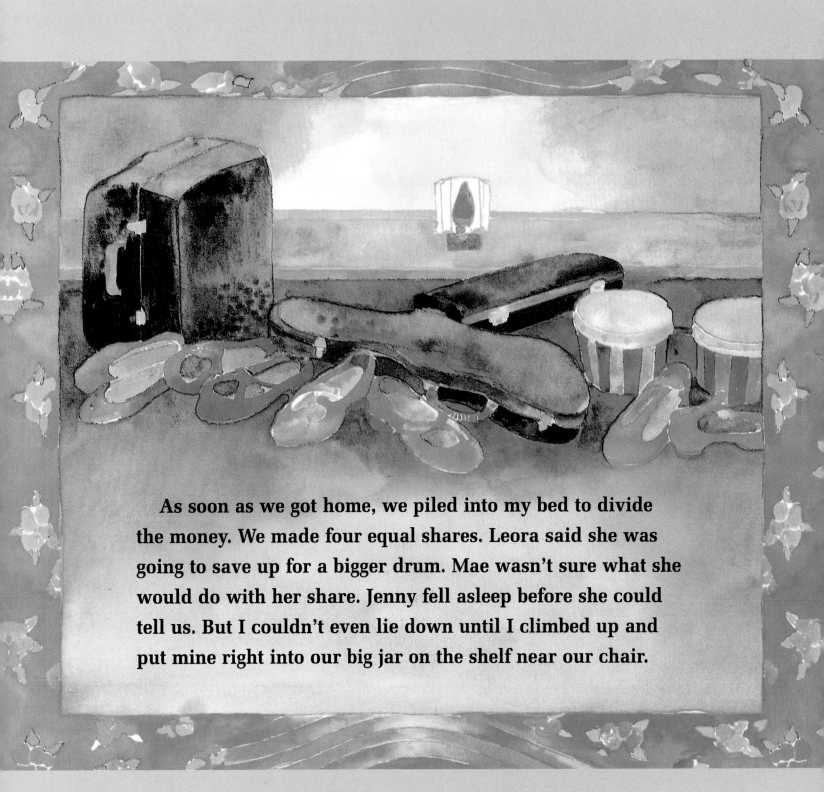

As soon as we got home, we piled into my bed to divide the money. We made four equal shares. Leora said she was going to save up for a bigger drum. Mae wasn't sure what she would do with her share. Jenny fell asleep before she could tell us. But I couldn't even lie down until I climbed up and put mine right into our big jar on the shelf near our chair.

from Tomie dePaola's
Book of Poems

SOURCE

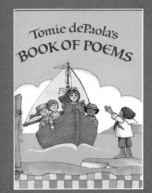

Tomie dePaola's
BOOK OF POEMS

Poetry
Collection

Celebration

by Alonzo Lopez
illustrated by Tomie dePaola

I shall dance tonight.
When the dusk comes crawling.
There will be dancing
    and feasting.
I shall dance with the others
    in circles,
        in leaps,
            in stomps.
Laughter and talk
    will weave into the night,
Among the fires
    of my people.
Games will be played
And I shall be
    a part of it.

Cast and Crew

Performances combine the talents of many people.

Be amazed at all the different acts in one circus. Then look at a poster about a very different circus.

Follow three pigs step by step in the making of a puppet show.

Meet the woman who brings out the best in people on the stage and behind it.

CIRCUS GIRL MICHAEL GARLAND

Alice is a circus girl. Everyone in her family is in the circus. Alice's mother walks the tightrope, and her father is a clown.

70

Alice and her mother and father live in a trailer.
They ride from town to town.
The circus travels around in a caravan filled
with people, animals, and all the equipment,
including the big tent—packed up for the ride.

When the circus comes to a new town, the elephants are paraded through the streets. Circus people put up signs and give out handbills to let everyone know when the show will begin.

Before the show, there is so
much work to be done.
Circus men put up the tent.
The performers practice
their acts, and the animals are
washed and brushed.
All the circus people help,
including Alice.

The show people put on their costumes, and the clowns paint their faces. Alice can't decide what she wants to be when she grows up—a tightrope walker or a clown.

With a roll of the drums, the band starts to play. The show is ready to begin! The ringmaster, Alice's grandfather, leads the elephants into the big tent, followed by clowns, fancy horses, jugglers, acrobats, and all the others, in a grand procession around the three rings.

The townspeople cheer!
The children shout!

80

Then suddenly, the music stops. The ringmaster leaps into the center ring. "Ladies and gentlemen, and children of all ages…" he says in a loud voice, announcing the acts—something different in each ring.

Everyone loves the Famous Dancing Bears.
The biggest bear can even ride a motorcycle!

The Flying Gazpacho Brothers are Alice's uncles.
Their skill and balance astound the audience!

Alice holds the hoop for her Auntie Anne's Amazing Performing Trick Dogs. Alice is so excited!

The lion tamer is very brave. When he cracks his whip, all the lions and tigers sit up and roll over.

The last and greatest act of all are the elephants. They entertain the audience with many clever feats. And then they lead the closing parade around the three rings. Other circus performers join them and wave good-bye. The townspeople cheer! The children shout! And then they go home.

The rings are swept clean, and the animals are back
in their pens and cages. The work is done.
The hungry circus people sit down to eat the dinner
that Alice's grandmother has cooked for them.

Everyone is tired, especially Alice. Her father reads
her a bedtime story before she goes to sleep. Alice
has to get up early in the morning because the
circus is going to another town—maybe yours!

Posters let us know that the circus is coming soon.

Lincoln Center

OCT 20 – JAN 8

BIG APPLE CIRCUS IS A NOT-FOR-PROFIT PERFORMING ARTS ORGANIZATION.

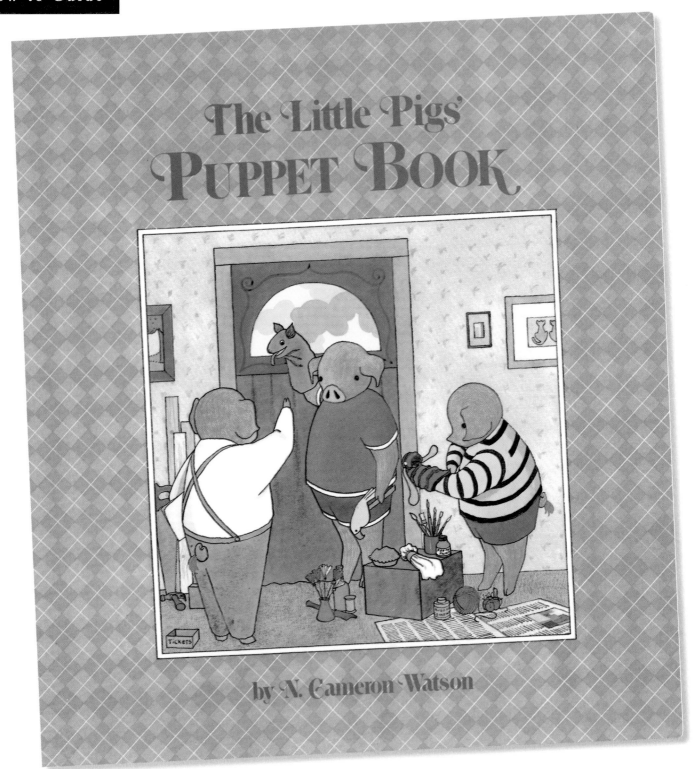

The Little Pigs'
PUPPET BOOK

by N. Cameron Watson

It is raining. The three brothers stare out the window.

"Bother!" says Charles.

"What a gloomy day," grunts Ralph.

"We could always read," remarks Bertram.

"I have a better idea," exclaims Charles. "Let's put on a puppet show!"

"First," says Bertram, "we have to make some puppets."
Each pig has a plan. Charles uses a sock for his puppet.
Bertram starts with a cardboard tube. Ralph decides on a
jaw puppet.

When the puppets are finished, the pigs confer on
story ideas. Charles wants to make up a story as they
go along. Bertram would prefer using a fairy tale.

The brothers finally agree on an original plot.
Ralph writes a script on his computer.

The pigs begin to rehearse. Ralph gets grumpy when Charles can't remember his lines. Charles thinks Ralph is too bossy. But Bertram keeps them going, and finally the play comes together nicely.

"How about building a stage?" says Ralph. Charles wants to set up a quick stage behind the table. Ralph suggests using a box. Bertram insists on making a stage to fit in the doorway. They all get to work.

The stage looks beautiful. "Bertram was right," admits Ralph.

"A stage like that needs some proper scenery," says Charles. He gathers his materials and begins.

"Then we'll need music, programs, tickets, and, of course, some refreshments," pronounces Bertram. He makes up the programs and tickets while Charles retires backstage to set everything up. Ralph goes to the kitchen to prepare some special treats.

The show begins. Charles is nervous, but then he
speaks his first line, and the performance is off to a
promising start. The audience is enthralled.

After the show, everyone stays for refreshments.
Charles's wonderful puppet is passed around. Bertram's
fine design and lettering on the programs are admired.

Several older pigs approach Ralph and give the
budding young author their congratulations. The
evening has been a great success.

Outside it is dark, and the sky is clearing.
Tomorrow will be a fine, sunny day. But the
brothers are eagerly awaiting the next rainy day
and what it might bring.

102

Special Effects

Lighting

Make room dark. Light only the stage opening, so attention will be focused there. Set up one light on each side of stage front. Make sure they do not block view of stage. Use:

 clamp-on spotlights

floor lamps

a flashlight
(held by a friend)

stage front
light *light*
seats

Bulb Color	Mood/Effect
white	normal/daylight
yellow	warm/coziness
blue	cold/moonlight
red	hot/scariness

Music

Use music to set the mood of the play and of each scene.

 piano

 recorder

 drum

 homemade rattle
(coins in a jar)

 *tape*
recorder

Sound Effects

Use your imagination! Here are some ideas:

thunder: drum; rattle a cookie sheet

crash: clang pots and utensils together

engine: coffee grinder or blender

thud: slap hand on floor

wind: blow over a bottle

footsteps: tap fingers on floor

Props

Make props from materials around the house, or use real objects. For example:

car: cardboard mounted on a flat stick, held from below

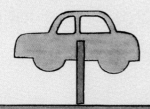

soda can: cardboard tube with added bottom and top

paintbrush: use a real one

flower: tissue paper, wooden skewer, and wire

Judith Martin

Theater Director

Curtain up!
On with the show!

Would you wear a costume made from paper bags? The Paper Bag Players do! They are a theater company that creates plays for children. They really do make their costumes from paper and cardboard.

Before children come to see a play, Judith Martin, the director, has a lot of work to do.

104

Questions

for Judith Martin

Here's how director Judith Martin works with her team to put on plays.

Q **How do you get your ideas for plays?**

A I try to think about what would make children laugh and what they would really like to see. Sometimes I go to schools and do theater with the children. They have many ideas about what makes a good play.

Q **What happens after you decide on an idea?**

A I write the script with all the lines that the actors will say. They practice their lines while I watch.

Q **Who else works on the play?**

A While the actors are practicing, our artist makes the props—all from paper or cardboard. I also tell her what kinds of costumes the actors need. Our musician writes and plays the music for the show and teaches it to the actors.

Q **What's the day of the first performance like?**

A The actors look great in their costumes. They know their lines and the music. And now it's the audience's turn to be part of the team. At some point in the play, the children are invited to join in somehow—maybe to dance!

Judith Martin's Tips for Young Directors

1 Work with your group to find a good story or write one about something funny that really happened.

2 Use homemade or old clothes for costumes.

3 Clear part of a room for a stage, and set up chairs for your audience.

Showtime!

Clear plans and directions help team members create projects.

Find out how much hard work goes into any movie that you see!

Choose a character you want to be in this read-aloud play. Then see where the ideas for the costumes came from.

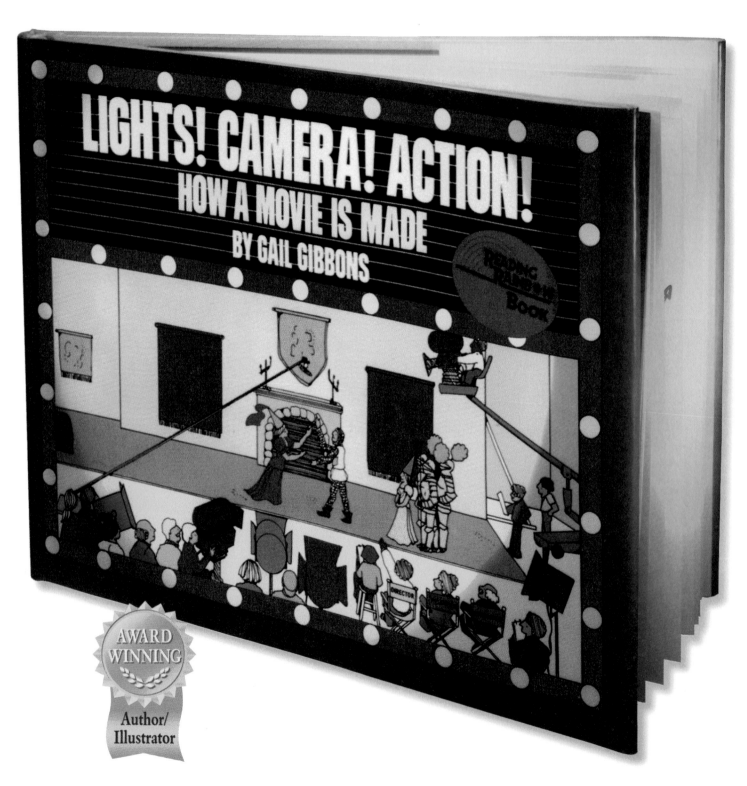

The story is perfect! It is exactly what the
movie producers have been looking for. They
want to take the story and make it into a movie.

The producers hire the people they will need to get started.

It could take millions of dollars to make the movie.
The producers describe their project to people who
might lend them money. That's how they get their
"financial backing."

A major movie studio also likes the project. They will
back the movie, too. And when the movie is finished,
they will rent out copies to movie theaters.

Step 1: Pre-production...

Now the work begins. The producers hire a scriptwriter. It takes a long time to turn a story into a script, or screenplay. All the dialogue for the actresses and actors is written in the script along with technical directions for lighting, camera angles, and scene changes.

Next, the casting director is hired. She finds actors
and actresses to play the leading parts. Sometimes the
people chosen are very famous...stars!

There are tryouts for the smaller parts.

The producers need to find just the right locations
for the different scenes. Then the production manager
makes a schedule for filming them.

Sketches are made.

The pre-production crew is bigger now.
The different departments work to get everything
ready. The costume designers, the lighting technicians,

the property department, the set designers,

the sound technicians, and the special effects
department rush to meet the production deadline.

The actresses and actors rehearse...

and rehearse their lines.

Finally, after months of work, everyone and everything is ready. It is time for the different scenes to be filmed.

They will not be shot in the order of the script. All the scenes in the same location, or on the same set, will be shot together. It is easier and costs less that way. When the filming is over, the scenes will be put together in order again.

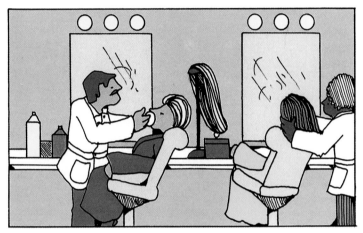

The actresses and actors arrive early each morning.
In the dressing rooms, makeup artists and hair
stylists get them ready for the day's shooting.
Wardrobe assistants help them into their costumes.

Meanwhile, over on the set, the camera operators are in position. The sound technicians are adjusting their equipment. The lighting technicians, called gaffers, have set up the lights.

The actors and actresses come in.

The scene is rehearsed one last time.

Step 2: Production...

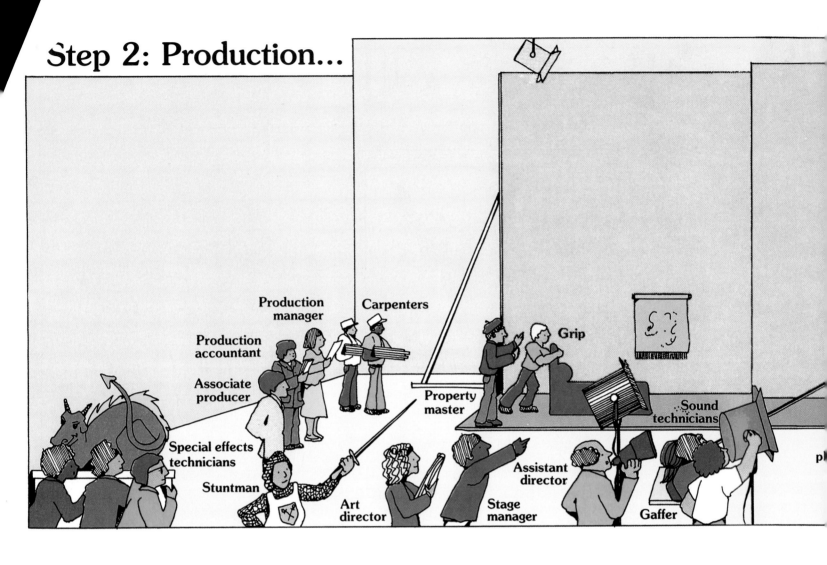

Everything looks right.

The director gives a signal. The assistant director yells,
"Quiet on the set!"

Camera
operator

Script-
writer

Set
designer

Makeup
artist

Hair
stylist

Costume
designer

DIRECTOR

PRODUCER

PRODUCER

Continuity
expert

Gaffer

Director of
photography

Chief
camera
operator

Production begins.
Lights! Camera! Action!

The director yells, "Cut!" Somebody missed
a line.

They reshoot the scene until it is perfect.

"Print it!" the director yells. He likes the take.

At the end of the day, all the takes are rushed to the film processing lab to be printed.

Each day's film is called a daily. Every morning the producers and director view the dailies from the day before.

Step 3: Post-production...

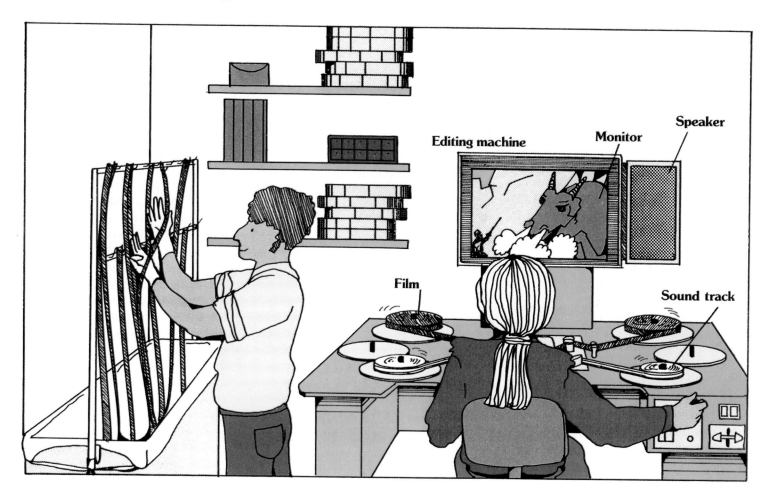

Once all the scenes have been shot, the film editors take over. They go through the reels and reels of film and select what they need. If it isn't just right, it is out.

The edited film is spliced together in the order of the scenes in the script.

The producers and director view the film. They all agree—it's just what they want. It works!

Dubbing console

Next, music must be added to the sound track.
A composer is hired. The music he creates will set
the mood for the film.

Any mistakes in the dialogue can be corrected now.

Mixers put the music, dialogue, and sound effects
together.

Then the complete sound track will be added to
the film.

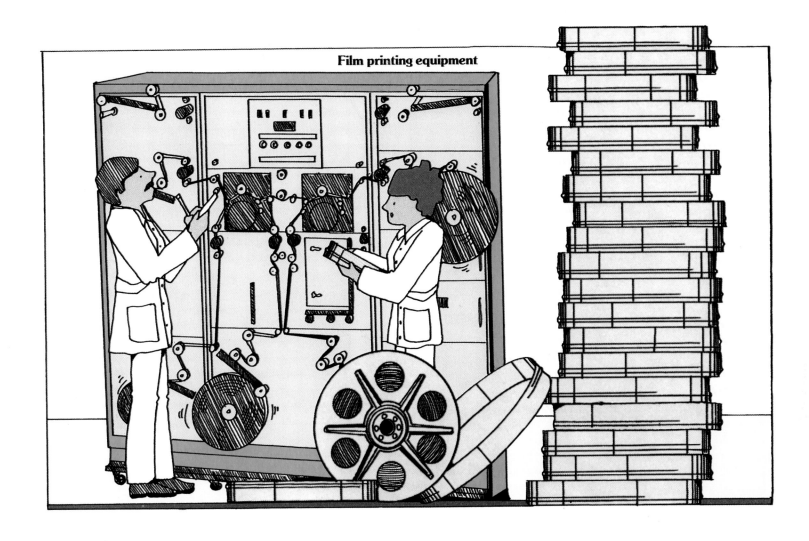

Film printing equipment

The movie is completed.

The first print, called an answer print, is made and given one final check. Then thousands of copies, called release prints, are made.

The movie studio will rent out these copies to the
movie theaters. For months, the studio has been
advertising the movie and stirring up interest with
a big publicity campaign.

The premier showing is held at a big city theater. The stars are there. All the people who made the movie are there, too.

Fans and movie critics come to the glamorous event.

The audience waits.

The lights go out and the movie begins.

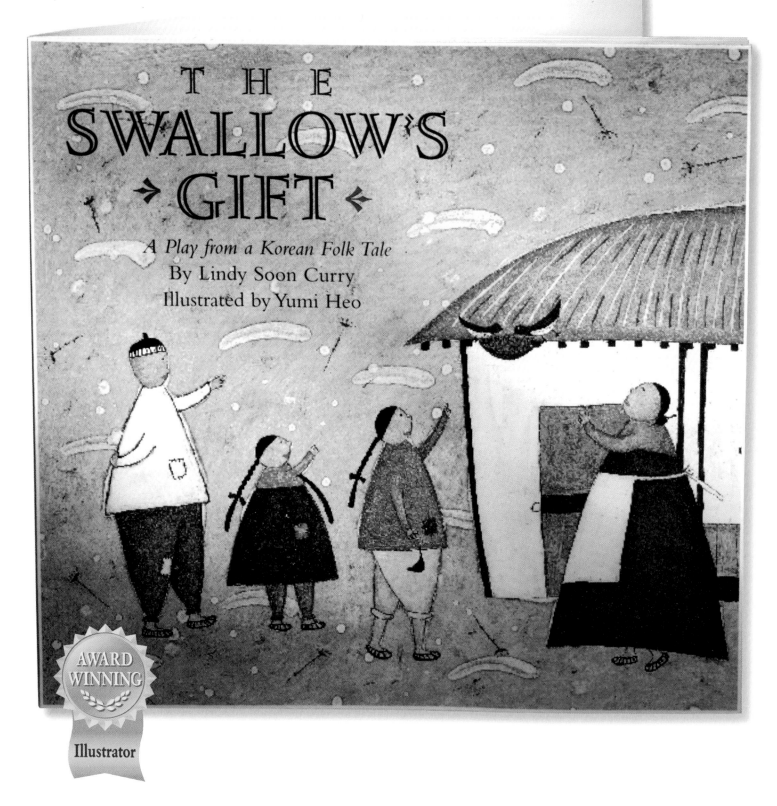

THE SWALLOW'S GIFT

A Play from a Korean Folk Tale
By Lindy Soon Curry
Illustrated by Yumi Heo

AWARD WINNING

Illustrator

Narrator
Nolbu, selfish older brother
Hungbu, kind younger brother
Mother, wife of Hungbu
Sister, daughter of Hungbu
Brother, son of Hungbu
Swallow

NARRATOR

Long ago in old Korea, two brothers lived together in a large house that their father had built. For many years they got along well. Then one winter day Nolbu got angry and ordered his younger brother Hungbu to move out.

Our play begins as Hungbu and his family set out in search of a new place to live.

SISTER

We have been walking for such a
long time.

BROTHER

I'm so cold and tired. Where will we
sleep tonight?

HUNGBU

Don't worry children. Here is a shack.
You gather leaves and branches.
Mother and I will patch the cracks and
make the house cozy and warm.

MOTHER

By working together, we'll make it
through the winter. But each of us
must help.

SISTER

I'll help clean the house.

BROTHER

I'll gather firewood.

NARRATOR

After a long cold winter, Hungbu and his family were glad to see spring arrive. They planted a garden and watched a pair of swallows build a nest on their roof. One day while they were gardening . . .

BROTHER

Look! This baby swallow fell out of the nest in our roof. I think its leg is broken.

HUNGBU

Baby swallow, don't be afraid. I'll help you. Let me bandage your leg with this cloth.

(He takes a piece of cloth and wraps it around the bird's leg.)

SWALLOW
Thank you. That feels much better.

BROTHER
Here's a bowl of water. Please drink some and get well quickly.

SISTER
Little swallow, eat some sesame seeds. They will make you strong.

SWALLOW
Ah! I feel better already.

MOTHER
You may sleep in this basket until you are strong enough to fly again.

SWALLOW
I'll always remember your kindness.

NARRATOR
The swallow was soon well enough to fly away. But one year later, the little bird returned to thank Hungbu and his family.

BROTHER
Father! There's the swallow with the crooked leg. It's hopping up to you.

HUNGBU
It has a pumpkin seed in its beak.

(He takes the seed from the bird.)

Thank you, swallow.

SWALLOW
This is a gift to thank you for taking care of me.

MOTHER
We'll plant it right away. I'll dig the hole.

SISTER
I'll cover the seed with dirt.

BROTHER
I'll water it and see that it is weeded.

NARRATOR

That night as the family slept, the swallow's seed sprouted, and it grew and grew. In the morning, Hungbu and his family awoke to an amazing sight.

MOTHER

Look outside! There's a big green plant . . .

SISTER

. . . with three yellow blossoms . . .

BROTHER

. . . that are turning into yellow pumpkins!

(Hungbu goes away and returns with a long saw.)

HUNGBU

Children, if you will help Mother and me, we can saw through this big pumpkin.

NARRATOR

And so they pushed and pulled and pushed and pulled until the first pumpkin fell open.

MOTHER
I see something glittering inside!

HUNGBU
Gold!

SISTER
Rubies!

BROTHER
Emeralds!

MOTHER
Let's open the
second pumpkin.

NARRATOR
They pushed and pulled on the saw.

BROTHER
I hear something rattling!

NARRATOR
And the second pumpkin fell open.

HUNGBU
Rice! Thousands of grains of rice!

MOTHER
Now we can eat, eat, eat!

BROTHER
Until our bellies are full, full, full!

SISTER
Let's open the third pumpkin.

NARRATOR
Once again, they pushed and pulled
until the third and last pumpkin
fell open.

MOTHER
Oooh! Yards and yards of silk! Let's
make beautiful clothes and stroll
into town.

NARRATOR
News traveled fast. When Nolbu heard about his brother's good fortune, he went to visit Hungbu.

NOLBU
How did you get all these riches?

HUNGBU
We took care of a swallow with a broken leg. It rewarded us with a seed that grew pumpkins filled with wonderful things. Come live with us, brother. There is plenty for everyone.

NOLBU
No. I'll find my own fortune.

NARRATOR
And Nolbu stormed off to search for a swallow.

148

NOLBU

Here's a swallow with a crooked leg.

(Nolbu quickly and roughly ties a cloth around the bird's leg.)

NOLBU

Now fly away and bring me back a seed. Make me richer than my brother.

SWALLOW

Ouch, you hurt me! I'll always remember this.

NARRATOR

The following spring, the bird returned to Nolbu and brought him a seed.

SWALLOW

Here's your reward as you wished.

NOLBU

I'll be rich, rich, rich!

NARRATOR

Nolbu planted his seed and it grew just as fast as Hungbu's did, but only two pumpkins sprouted from it instead of three. Nolbu had trouble cutting the pumpkins open because he was all alone. He had no one to help him.

(The first pumpkin breaks open.)

NOLBU

This pumpkin is rotten! It smells terrible! I must open the second one. Perhaps that one will be full of money.

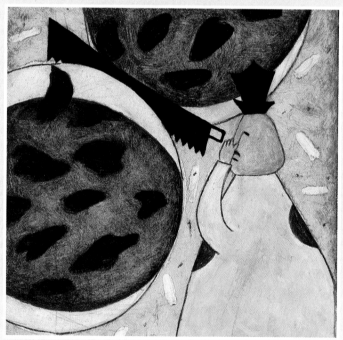

(Nolbu saws the second pumpkin until it falls open.)

NOLBU

Yuck! Spiders and snakes and scorpions!
They are crawling over everything!
I can't live in this house anymore.
Maybe Hungbu will let me live with
him after all.

NARRATOR

Nolbu returned to his brother's house
and knocked on the door.

HUNGBU

Welcome, brother! Please come in.

NOLBU

I am sorry for the way I treated you. Now my house is full of bugs and snakes. May I live with you?

HUNGBU

Yes, please join us. I'm sorry for what has happened to you.

NOLBU

I'll always work and share equally with you.

HUNGBU

That's the way our father wanted us to live.

NARRATOR

From that day on, the two brothers lived together under the same roof happily ever after.

A Long Ago Look

SOURCE

Korean
Reference Book

Here's clothing that Korean men and women wore a long, long time ago. Koreans often wore light-colored pieces of clothing. What they wore depended upon how much money they had. Today in Korea, clothing like this from long ago is worn by older people on special holidays.

Glossary

accordion

a musical instrument with a keyboard played with one hand and a bellows pushed in and out with the other hand

She played a lively tune on her new **accordion**.

acrobats

performers who do exciting tricks, such as walking on a wire high above the ground

The **acrobats** fly through the air.

acrobats

actors

people who perform in plays, movies, or TV stories

The **actors** in this movie are very good.

actresses

women or girls who perform in plays, movies, or TV stories

We need three more **actresses** for our school play.

assistants

helpers

The doctor had two **assistants** who helped her take care of sick people.

clowns

performers who dress in funny clothes and do tricks to make people laugh

The **clowns** wore silly hats and shoes and big red noses.

clowns

composer

a person who makes up music

The **composer** sat at the piano to play his new song.

cowards

people who are afraid of anything that is dangerous or hard to do

They felt like **cowards** for not climbing all the way to the top.

danger

something that could hurt you

The rabbit crossing the busy road is in **danger**.

director

the person who tells the actors what to do in a movie or play

The **director** told the actor to speak louder.

dreadful

scary, terrible

The angry tiger was a **dreadful** thing to see.

drums

musical instruments played by beating with sticks

The musician moved his sticks quickly across his **drums.**

emeralds

emeralds

bright green jewels or the stones they are made from

Emeralds are worth a lot of money.

fiddle

a musical instrument played by moving a bow across the strings

He picked up the bow to play his **fiddle**.

fierce

wild and dangerous

Angry animals are sometimes **fierce**.

flute

a long, thin musical instrument played by blowing through one end and placing fingers over the holes

Her fingers were moving slowly as she played the **flute**.

flutes

fortune
a lot of money
The rich man gave some of his **fortune** to help poor people.

gruesome
scary and horrible
The monster's face was **gruesome**.

guitar
a musical instrument played by moving the fingers across the strings
The performer played the **guitar** and sang.

instrument
something used to make music
The piano is my favorite **instrument**.

jugglers

jugglers
performers who do tricks with things they throw and catch
The **jugglers** could keep four pins up in the air at one time.

kindness
being nice and helpful to others
The old woman was loved by all for her **kindness**.

performers
people who do something to entertain others
The jugglers, acrobats, and clowns are all **performers** in the circus.

producers
people who get a movie, show, or play ready to be seen
Producers hire the actors, writers, and directors for movies.

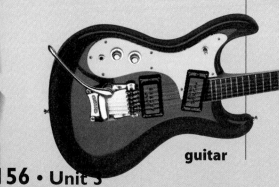
guitar

programs
small booklets that tell about a show
The **programs** tell who is in the play and what they will do.

rehearse
to practice a play or other show before presenting it to an audience
We had to **rehearse** our play many times.

rewarded
having received money or treats for good work or kind acts
The boy who saved the puppy was **rewarded** with ten dollars.

riches
money and things that are worth a lot of money
The king had jewels and other **riches**.

ringmaster
the person at the circus who tells about the performers
The **ringmaster** told us about the jugglers.

rubies
bright red jewels
The **rubies** in her necklace were beautiful.

scared
afraid, frightened
The cat was **scared** of falling in the water.

scenery
painted walls, hangings, or other things that are put on a stage to show where the play takes place
The **scenery** for the play showed the inside of the king's castle.

script
a written copy of what actors say in a play, movie, or TV or radio show
The actors had to read the **script** until they learned what to say.

stage
the place where actors, dancers, or singers perform
The singers and dancers were all on the **stage** at once.

technicians
people who can use or fix machines
The people who take care of the sound at a music show are **technicians**.

terror
strong fear
The hunter felt **terror** when the bear ran after him.

Authors and Illustrators

Gail Gibbons pages 110-137

Gail Gibbons used to work at a TV station. She had a lot of fun creating art for a children's show. This made her decide to write and illustrate a children's book. Now she works all the time on children's books about many different subjects. Books by Gibbons include *Weather Words and What They Mean* and *Beacons of Light: Lighthouses.*

Yumi Heo pages 138-152

Yumi Heo says that *The Swallow's Gift* is a tale she has known and loved since she was a little girl in Korea. Heo also remembers getting her first box of crayons. She was five then, and she has been creating colorful pictures ever since. Another tale with pictures by Heo is *The Rabbit's Judgment* by Suzanne Crowder Han.

Hans Wilhelm pages 10-35

Hans Wilhelm grew up in Bremen, Germany—the very same town in which *The Bremen Town Musicians* takes place! He says that he likes writing funny stories and drawing pictures to match. His book *Tyrone the Horrible* is about a dinosaur that is a bully. In *Bad, Bad Bunny Trouble*, a bunny who loves soccer plays a trick on three hungry foxes.

Vera B. Williams pages 36-64

Vera B. Williams wrote and illustrated her first book in high school. It was about a giant banana! Most of this author's books are about things that happened to her. She says that the character of Rosa reminds her of herself as a little girl. Two other books about Rosa and her family are *A Chair for My Mother* and *Something Special for Me.*

Acknowledgments

Grateful acknowledgment is made to the following sources for permission to reprint from previously published material. The publisher has made diligent efforts to trace the ownership of all copyrighted material in this volume and believes that all necessary permissions have been secured. If any errors or omissions have inadvertently been made, proper corrections will gladly be made in future editions.

Front cover: Illustration from RUBY THE COPYCAT by Peggy Rathmann. Illustration copyright © 1991 by Margaret Rathmann. Reprinted by permission of Scholastic Inc.

Back cover: Top: All photos © David S. Waitz for Scholastic Inc. Middle: Cover by Bill Mayer. Bottom: Photo: © Tracey Wheeler for Scholastic Inc. Border illustration: Anthony De Angelos.

Acknowledgments

Grateful acknowledgment is made to the following sources for permission to reprint from previously published material. The publisher has made diligent efforts to trace the ownership of all copyrighted material in this volume and believes that all necessary permissions have been secured. If any errors or omissions have inadvertently been made, proper corrections will gladly be made in future editions.

Unit Opener: all photos © David S. Waitz for Scholastic Inc.

Interior: "Ronald Morgan Goes to Bat" from RONALD MORGAN GOES TO BAT by Patricia Reilly Giff, illustrated by Susanna Natti. Text copyright © 1988 by Patricia Reilly Giff. Illustrations copyright © 1988 by Susanna Natti. Reprinted by permission of Viking Penguin, a division of Penguin Books USA Inc.

BABE RUTH: TM/© 1995 Family of Babe Ruth and the Babe Ruth Baseball League, Inc. Under license authorized by Curtis Management Group, Indianapolis, IN. *JUAN GONZALEZ:* Upper Deck and the card/hologram combination are trademarks of The Upper Deck Company, are reproduced with permission of The Upper Deck Company, are the exclusive property of The Upper Deck Company, and may not be reproduced without the express written consent of The Upper Deck Company. The Texas Rangers insignias depicted in this publication are reproduced with the permission of Major League Baseball Properties, are the exclusive property of the Texas Rangers, and may not be reproduced without their written consent. The Juan Gonzalez baseball card is also used by permission of Major League Baseball Players Association.

"Ruby the Copycat" from RUBY THE COPYCAT by Peggy Rathmann. Copyright © 1991 by Margaret Rathmann. Reprinted by permission of Scholastic Inc.

"I Can" by Mari Evans from SINGING BLACK published by Reed Visuals, 1979. Reprinted by permission of the author. Cover and illustration by Floyd Cooper from PASS IT ON: AFRICAN-AMERICAN POETRY FOR CHILDREN by Wade Hudson and Cheryl Hudson. Illustrations copyright © 1993 by Floyd Cooper. Published by Scholastic Inc. by arrangement with JUST US BOOKS. Reprinted by permission.

"Louanne Pig in Making the Team" from LOUANNE PIG IN MAKING THE TEAM by Nancy Carlson. Copyright © 1985 by Nancy Carlson. Reprinted by permission of Carolrhoda Books, Inc. All rights reserved.

GEORGE ANCONA: THEN & NOW by George Ancona. Copyright © 1996 by Scholastic Inc.

"Amazing Grace" from AMAZING GRACE by Mary Hoffman, illustrated by Caroline Binch. Text copyright © 1991 by Mary Hoffman. Illustrations copyright © 1991 by Caroline Binch. Reprinted by permission of Dial Books for Young Readers, a division of Penguin Books USA Inc.

Theatre program and cast list from PETER PAN is used by kind permission of The People's Light & Theatre Company.

Cover from A BIRTHDAY BASKET FOR TÍA by Pat Mora, illustrated by Cecily Lang. Illustration copyright © 1992 by Cecily Lang. Published by Simon & Schuster Books for Young Readers, Simon & Schuster Children's Publishing Division.

Cover from CHESTER'S WAY by Kevin Henkes. Illustration copyright © 1988 by Kevin Henkes. Published by Viking Penguin, a division of Penguin Books USA Inc.

Cover from FROG AND TOAD ARE FRIENDS by Arnold Lobel. Illustration copyright © 1970 by Arnold Lobel. Published by HarperCollins Publishers.

Cover from MAX FOUND TWO STICKS by Brian Pinkney. Illustration copyright © 1994 by Brian Pinkney. Published by Simon & Schuster Books for Young Readers, Simon and Schuster Children's Publishing Division.

Photography and Illustration Credits

Selection Opener Photographs by David S. Waitz Photography/Alleycat Design, Inc.

Photos: p. 3 br: © Gerry Lewin for Scholastic Inc. pp. 8-9 c: © Stanley Bach for Scholastic Inc. p. 10 cl: © Stanley Bach for Scholastic Inc.; br: © Dick Clintsman for Scholastic Inc.; tl: © Ken Karp for Scholastic Inc. p. 11 tl: © Nicole Katano for Scholastic Inc.; tc: Stanley Bach for Scholastic Inc.; br: © Tom Raymond for Scholastic Inc. p. 12 tl, bl: © Tom Raymond for Scholastic Inc.; tr: © Dick Clintsman for Scholastic Inc. p. 13 c: © Stanley Bach for Scholastic Inc. p. 14 cr, cl: © Nicole Katano for Scholastic Inc. p. 43 bc: © Bob Lorenz for Scholastic Inc. pp. 44-45 all: © Stanley Bach for Scholastic Inc. pp. 94-95 all: © Gerry Lewin for Scholastic Inc. p. 96 tr: © Mitchell Layton/DUOMO; bl: © Gerry Lewin for Scholastic Inc. pp. 96-97 bc: © John Bessler for Scholastic Inc., © Bruce Thorson film strip of Thorson photos. p. 97 cr: © Bruce Thorson. pp. 98-99 c: © Jade Albert/FPG International Corp. p. 100 c: © Efrain Ancona; br: © Marina Ancona. p. 101 tc, c: Courtesy George Ancona. p. 102 tl: © Efrain Ancona; br: © George Ancona. p. 103 c: © George Ancona from the book MAN AND MUSTANG, Macmillan. p. 104 all: © Efrain Ancona. p. 105 c: © George Ancona. p. 106 c: © Efrain Ancona. p. 107: © Marina Ancona. p. 108 c: © Efrain Ancona. p. 109 c: © George Ancona. p. 110 c: Courtesy George Ancona. p. 111 c: © Nelson Barbosa Dos Santos. p. 112 bl: © Fausto Diaz Triay; tr: © George Ancona; c: Courtesy George Ancona. p. 113 bc: © Beth Cummins. p. 114 tl, bl: © George Ancona; tr: © Thomas Pinot. p. 115 tl, cr: © George Ancona; bl: © Arleia Martins. p. 136 c: © Blanche Mackey for Scholastic Inc.; cr: © Bie Bostrom for Scholastic Inc. p. 137 all: Mark Garvin/Courtesy of People's Light Theater. p. 138 br: © Joseph Nettis/Photo Researchers, Inc. p. 139 tr: © John Lei for Scholastic Inc; br: © Gerry Lewin for Scholastic Inc. p. 140 cl: © Nicole Katano for Scholastic Inc. p. 141 bc: © Tony Freeman/Photo Edit; tr: © Bonnie Rauch/Photo Researchers, Inc.; cl: © David S. Waitz for Scholastic Inc. p. 142 br: © Mark Lafavor. p. 143 br: © Tornberg Associates

Illustrations: pp. 2-3: Jackie Snider; p.42: Brian Dugan; pp. 136-137: Mary Thelen.

Acknowledgments

Grateful acknowledgment is made to the following sources for permission to reprint from previously published material. The publisher has made diligent efforts to trace the ownership of all copyrighted material in this volume and believes that all necessary permissions have been secured. If any errors or omissions have inadvertently been made, proper corrections will gladly be made in future editions.

Unit Opener: Bill Mayer.

Interior: "Truman's Aunt Farm" from TRUMAN'S AUNT FARM by Jama Kim Rattigan, illustrated by G. Brian Karas. Text copyright © 1994 by Jama Kim Rattigan. Illustrations copyright © 1994 by G. Brian Karas. Reprinted by permission of Houghton Mifflin Co. All rights reserved.

"Ants" from YELLOW BUTTER PURPLE JELLY RED JAM BLACK BREAD by Mary Ann Hoberman. Text copyright © 1981 by Mary Ann Hoberman. Published by Viking Press. Reprinted by permission of Gina Maccoby Literary Agency.

"The Paper Crane" from THE PAPER CRANE by Molly Bang. Copyright © 1985 by Molly Garrett Bang. Reprinted by permission of Greenwillow Books, a division of William Morrow & Company, Inc.

"Pigsty" from PIGSTY by Mark Teague. Copyright © 1994 by Mark Teague. Reprinted by permission of Scholastic Inc. MONOPOLY® is a registered trademark of Tonka Corporation for its real estate trading game and elements. Copyright © 1934, 1992 Parker Brothers, a division of Tonka Corporation. Used with permission.

"Belling the Cat" and cover from ONCE IN A WOOD, adapted and illustrated by Eve Rice. Copyright © 1979 by Eve Rice. Reprinted by permission of Greenwillow Books, a division of William Morrow & Company, Inc.

"Kids Helping Kids: Friends" (September 1992) and "Kids Helping Kids: When the Sitter Just Sits" (January/February 1993) from U*S*Kids®, a Weekly Reader magazine. Copyright © 1992 by Children's Better Health Institute, Benjamin Franklin Literary & Medical Society, Inc. Indianapolis, IN. Reprinted by permission.

THE CODE KING by Bill Dallas Lewis. Copyright © 1996 by Scholastic Inc.

"Martí and the Mango" from MARTI AND THE MANGO by Daniel Moreton. Copyright © 1993 by Daniel Moreton. Reprinted by permission of Stewart, Tabori & Chang, Publishers, NY.

"A Fair Share" and cover from FRACTION ACTION by Loreen Leedy. Copyright © 1994 by Loreen Leedy. All rights reserved. Reprinted by permission of Holiday House, Inc.

Cover from MISS NELSON HAS A FIELD DAY by Harry Allard, illustrated by James Marshall. Illustration copyright © 1985 by James Marshall. Published by Houghton Mifflin Company.

Cover from NEW SHOES FOR SILVIA by Johanna Hurwitz, illustrated by Jerry Pinkney. Illustration copyright © 1993 by Jerry Pinkney. Published by William Morrow & Company, Inc.

Cover from PET SHOW by Ezra Jack Keats. Illustration copyright © 1972 by Ezra Jack Keats. Published by Aladdin Books, Simon & Schuster Children's Publishing Division.

Cover from ZOMO THE RABBIT: A TRICKSTER TALE FROM WEST AFRICA by Gerald McDermott. Illustration copyright © 1992 by Gerald McDermott. Published by Harcourt Brace Jovanovich, Publishers.

Photography and Illustration Credits

Selection Opener Photographs by David S. Waitz Photography/Alleycat Design, Inc. for Scholastic Inc.

Photos: pp. 2-3 c: © James Lukoski for Scholastic Inc. p. 3 br: © James Lukoski for Scholastic Inc. p. 52 tr: © John Lei for Scholastic Inc. p. 52 bl, cl: © James Lukoski for Scholastic Inc. p. 53 c, tr: © John Lei for Scholastic Inc. p. 54 br, cl: © John Lei for Scholastic Inc. tr: © John Bessler for Scholastic Inc. p. 55 c: © James Lukoski for Scholastic Inc.; tr: © John Lei for Scholastic Inc. pp. 86-89: © Julie Bidwell. p. 107 cr: © Mark Lyons for Scholastic Inc. p. 138 bl: © Stan Sholik/FPG International Corp. p. 139 br: © Eduardo Garcia/FPG International Corp.; tc: © Ray Coleman/Photo Researchers, Inc. p. 140 cl: © Photo Researchers, Inc. p. 141 bc: © R. Pleasant/FPG International Corp. p. 142 br: © Holiday House; bl: © Courtesy of William Morrow & Company. p. 143 br: Courtesy of Scholastic Trade Department, bl: Courtesy of Daniel Moreton

Illustrations: pp. 2-3: Jackie Snider; pp. 8-9: Dave Jolly; p. 31: Lisa Adams; pp. 56-57: Dave Jolly; pp. 80-85: Drew Brook-Cormack; pp. 90-91: Dave Jolly.

Acknowledgments

Grateful acknowledgment is made to the following sources for permission to reprint from previously published material. The publisher has made diligent efforts to trace the ownership of all copyrighted material in this volume and believes that all necessary permissions have been secured. If any errors or omissions have inadvertently been made, proper corrections will gladly be made in future editions.

Unit Opener: Photo: © Tracey Wheeler for Scholastic Inc. Border illustration: Anthony De Angelos.

Interior: The "Bremen Town Musicians" from THE BREMEN TOWN MUSICIANS by Hans Wilhelm. Copyright © 1992 by Hans Wilhelm, Inc. Reprinted by permission of Scholastic Inc.

"Music, Music For Everyone" from MUSIC, MUSIC FOR EVERYONE by Vera B. Williams. Copyright © 1984 by Vera B. Williams. By permission of Greenwillow Books, a division of William Morrow & Company, Inc.

"Celebration" by Alonzo Lopez from WHISPERING WIND by Terry Allen. Text copyright © 1972 by the Institute of American Indian Arts. Used by permission of Doubleday, a division of Bantam Doubleday Dell Publishing Group, Inc. Cover and illustrations by Tomie dePaola from TOMIE DEPAOLA'S BOOK OF POEMS. Illustrations copyright © 1988 by Tomie dePaola. Reprinted by permission of G. P. Putnam's Sons.

"Circus Girl" from CIRCUS GIRL by Michael Garland. Copyright © 1993 by Michael Garland. Used by permission of Dutton Children's Books, a division of Penguin Books USA Inc.

Selections and cover from THE LITTLE PIGS' PUPPET BOOK by N. Cameron Watson. Copyright © 1990 by N. Cameron Watson. Reprinted by permission of Little, Brown and Company.

"Lights! Camera! Action! How a Movie is Made" from LIGHTS! CAMERA! ACTION! HOW A MOVIE IS MADE by Gail Gibbons. Copyright © 1985 by Gail Gibbons. Reprinted by permission of HarperCollins Publishers.

THE SWALLOW'S GIFT by Lindy Soon Curry, illustrated by Yumi Heo. Copyright © 1996 by Scholastic Inc.

Cover from BASEBALL BALLERINA by Kathryn Cristaldi, illustrated by Abby Carter. Illustration copyright © 1992 by Abby Carter. Published by Random House, Inc.

Cover from THE BUNNY PLAY by Loreen Leedy. Illustration copyright © 1988 by Loreen Leedy. Published by Holiday House, Inc.

Cover from SHEEP DREAMS by Arthur A. Levine, illustrated by Judy Lanfredi. Illustration copyright © 1993 by Judy Lanfredi. Published by Dial Books for Young Readers, a division of Penguin Books USA Inc.

Cover from SONG AND DANCE MAN by Karen Ackerman, illustrated by Stephen Gammell. Illustration copyright © 1988 by Stephen Gammell. Published by Alfred A. Knopf, Inc.

Photography and Illustration Credits

Selection Opener Photographs by David S. Waitz Photography/Alleycat Design, Inc.

Photos: p. 3 br: © Andrew M. Levine for Scholastic Inc. pp.2-3: © Scott Heiser/Courtesy, The Paper Bag Players. pp.8-9: © Stanley Bach for Scholastic Inc. pp.8-9 background: © Christian Michaels/FPG International Corp. pp.66-67 c: © Stanley Bach for Scholastic Inc. pp.92-92 c: Courtesy of Big Apple Circus. p. 104 bl: © Martha Swope for Scholastic Inc.; tl: © Scott Heiser/Courtesy, The Paper Bag Players. pp.104-105 tc: © Andrew M. Levine for Scholastic Inc. p. 105 br: Andrew M. Levine for Scholastic Inc.p. 106 cl: Martha Swope for Scholastic Inc. pp. 106-107 bc: Martha Swope for Scholastic Inc. p. 107 tr,cr: © Andrew M. Levine for Scholastic Inc.; br: © Martha Swope for Scholastic Inc. pp. 108-109: © Stanley Bach for Scholastic Inc. p. 153 cr, cl, tr: Courtesy of Yegyong Sanopsa/Pascal Andre for Scholastic Inc. p. 154 tc: © Haroldo de Faria/FPG International Corp.; br: © M. Keller/The Stock Market. p. 155 c: © Carl Frank, 1972/Photo Researchers, Inc.; br: © Kathy Sloane/Photo Researchers, Inc. p. 156 tc: © Michael Newman/PhotoEdit; bl: © David S. Waitz for Scholastic Inc. p. 158 bl: © Courtesy of Holiday House; p. 158 br: © Courtesy of Yumi Heo; p. 159 Hans Wilhelm: Courtesy of Scholastic Trade Department; br: © Courtesy of William Morrow & Company.

Illustrations: pp. 2-3: Jackie Snider; p. 92: Brian Dugan.